Pedigree®

Published 2010. Pedigree Books Ltd
Beech Hill House, Walnut Gardens, Exeter, Devon EX4 4DH
books@pedigreegroup.co.uk | www.pedigreebooks.com

Contents

£12.99

Good Day worthy adversary and welcome the 2011 Family Guy Christmas Annual. You are no doubt sitting comfortably, surrounded by snoring relatives and discarded chocolate wrappers ready to read dirty words like poop.

Well, we won't disappoint you. There'll be plenty of poop in this edition, don't worry about that. In fact, there'll be more poop in this Annual than one of Peter's dreams, and there's a lot of poop in Peter's dreams!

If this is the first time you've ever picked up a Family Guy piece of snot, then you are in for quite a treat. On that, if you every get a peanut stuck in your ear, simply fill your ear with chocolate and it will come out a treat. If you're hoping for anything better than that, buddy, take a hike, okay?

Meet the Griffins

Let us introduce you to Peter Griffin, the lovable idiot and alpha male of middle-class New Englanders, the Griffins. Peter is a man who believes in speaking about a week before he thinks… "Mr. Weed? This is Peter Griffin. I will not be coming to work today, I was in a terrible plane crash. My entire family was killed and I am a vegetable."

"Hello Sally, h-hey it's Peter Griffin. Yeah, that's right, Senior Prom, yeah it's been a while… so listen, um, I just found out that I'm retarded and um… I'm just calling to let you know that uh, you might want to get yourself tested."

Peter's long-suffering wife is Lois, a former Miss Teen Rhode Island who rules the roost while teetering on the edge of a nervous breakdown. Lois was born into the wealthy Pewterschmidt family from Newport, Rhode Island and met Peter when he was a towel boy at the family country club. She once mentioned that she has a degree from Kent State University… "one time, the National Guard came and shot some of my friends" … she teaches piano and loves naughty bedroom stuff… "Cleveland, don't you see this is why your wife left you? You don't have enough passion. Sometimes a woman wants to see a man be a man. You gotta push back a little. (Lois starts shaking.) You gotta get a little rough. OH GOD!!!!!! (Pulls down pants and Lois bends over.) Peter HIT ME!"

Peter and Lois have three children, Meg, a frumpy teenager who is the family's suicidal

punch bag. Middle child Chris has inherited his father's infinite stupidity while concealing impressive, and diverse, artistic ability. One-year-old Stewie is diabolically clever, constantly plotting ways to kill his mother. And then there's Brian, a Mensa member who loves martinis, dumb blondes, marijuana and parked cars. Brian's on-off girlfriend Jillian is a sexy, dizzy thing who just doesn't understand why Adolf Hitler wasn't stopped.

Lois' father, Carter Pewterschmidt, is a billionaire industrialist. He hates Peter with a passion…

Peter at Christmas in front of the Pewterschmidt fireplace. Carter throws his pocket watch in front of the fireplace. Carter: "Oh, I dropped my watch. Peter, would you be a sport and fetch it for me?" Peter: "Sure thing, Mr. Pewterschmidt." Carter kicks Peter into the fire. Peter, screaming and on fire… *AHHHHHHHHHHH!*

Carter: "Oh dear, we've got to put that out!: Carter beats Peter with a log. Peter: "Ow Ow Ow Ow!" He is married to Barbara and has had three children - Lois, Carol, and murderous Patrick.

Brian's only family member is his flamboyantly gay cousin, Jasper who is married to a Filipino named Ricardo. Let's not talk about Peter's family. They're bad, Irish people.

The Griffins live amongst a caring, decent community full of paraplegics, bullies, sex maniacs, paedophiles and an insane mayor…

THE GRIFFINS LIVE AMONGST A CARING, DECENT COMMUNITY FULL OF PARAPLEGICS, GAYS, SEX MANIACS, PAEDOPHILES, BULLIES AND AN INSANE MAYOR. . .

Spooner Street

Peter's two closest friends are Quagmire and Joe. Quagmire is a man who finds sexual excitement in almost everything, apart from the use of the word 'rubbish' to mean 'garbage'.

"Hey guys, what's going on? I was just jerki … ed out of a deep sleep." "Fat chicks need love too… they just have to PAY!"

Joe Swanson received his paralysing injury at Christmas time while investigating a robbery at an orphanage, committed by a Grinch. Joe slid off the roof on a roller skate, injuring his spine and leaving him unable to walk. Joe is married to Bonnie, a calm and soft-spoken woman who was pregnant for, like, forever.

Mort and Muriel Goldman live next door with their son Neil. Mort's a Jewish pharmacist and not really that funny. But then he's Jewish so at least he has a comedy big nose. Down the road a little is Herbert, the Griffin's 'friendly', whistley-voiced old neighbour, who thinks Chris is just a big ol' sexy ball of teenage fun.

Quahog

The Mayor of Quahog, Mayor West is an eccentric, paranoid and frankly dangerous politician... "Today we are here to honour Joe Swanson for pulling my poor one-eyed cat Bootsy out of the old stove pipe of my Grandmother's cabin.... Sorry, Joe Swanson won the special people's decathlon and we're here to honour him."

At Quahog's Channel 5 News television station there's narcissistic anchorman Tom Tucker, sort of modelled after the cigarette spokesman from the 1940s commercials, and his slutty side kick Diane Simmons.

Tom Tucker's former wife Stacy became a hooker and his son has an upside down face. The Quahog Channel 5 News team is completed by Asian reporter

TODAY WE ARE HERE TO HONOUR JOE SWANSON FOR PULLING MY POOR ONE-EYED CAT BOOTSY OUT OF THE OLD STOVE PIPE OF MY GRANDMOTHER'S CABIN. . ..

Tricia Takanawa, Black-U-Weather forecast reporter Ollie Williams and some Hispanic woman,.. Jimana... Jima.. Ji...

Performance artist Bruce speaks in a calm, lispy drawn-out voice and once had a job as an emergency services operator...

"I think there's someone in my house!"

Bruce: "Oh, I envy that. I live alone. Nobody ever comes over my house."

"No! I mean there's somebody in my house right now!"

Bruce: "Well, maybe you'll want to put out some snacks or something. Doesn't have to be nothing fancy. You can even just open up a box of wheat thins and pour some in a bowl. Multi-Grain's always good."

"Oh my God! They're coming up the stairs!"

Bruce: "Oh, you're going to have to close that bedroom door if your bed's not made. Maybe, perhaps you could put on a video later and sneak upstairs to make that bed."

"Ahh!"

Bruce: "Oh, looks like they saw that bedroom."

There's Hispanic cleaner Consuela, the Head of the Maids' Union whose stock answer to almost anything is "Noooooooo...."

Carl is the manager of the Quahog Mini-Mart who loves eighties DVDs, Shamus is a tough fisherman with wood for arms and legs and Dr. Hartman who Peter accuses of rape, despite the fact he simply performed a normal prostate exam.

Peter's works at the Pawtucket Brewery. His boss is Angela, a staunch feminist who has a love-hate relationship with sexy Peter. Alongside Peter works Opie, a severely mentally disabled co-worker and ward of the state.

The Griffin kids go to James Woods Regional High School where school bully Connie D'Amico lays in wait and maths teacher Mr. Berler has a fear of vampires.

We've not even mentioned Death, God, Jesus, Horace, Evil Monkey, Ernie the Giant Chicken, Bertram and more famous faces than the Los Angeles drug rehabilitation programme.

Tis the season to be jolly, apparently, so join us as we take a Season Eight slanted look at Family Guy!

Welcome to DRUNKEN CLAMMERS The Clam!

Grab a drink, pull up a chair and join the locals!

No, The Drunken Clam is not a slutty, drunk, older, slightly trashy looking woman at the bar looking to pick up younger men, it's the local Quahog Bar.

The Clam is the perfect place for brawls and anti-semitism, racism and rudeness, a place not just to drown your sorrows but a place to put your foot on your sorrow's neck and scream 'I should not have attacked that schoolgirl'.

The Clam, resplendent with a neon sign showing a clam swigging from a bottle, is a place owned by Horace, a man who smiles about as much as a battery hen.

The Clam has had some misadventure. In *One if by Clam, Two if by Sea*, a hurricane decimates the place and it is taken over by Brit Nigel Pinchley who burns it down in an insurance scam and then returns to England.

Horace arrives back from Florida, claiming the place "stank" and buys back the pub. He returns the place to its former glory, much to the delight of Quahog.

In *Blind Ambition*, the bar burns to the ground (again) when God tries to impress a woman by lighting her cigarette with a thunderbolt. In *Don't Make Me Over*, the Clam becomes a Karaoke Bar, as the gang help Horace to put the bar back on its feet.

In *Meet the Quagmires*, Death shows up when Horace falls off his ladder in the Clam, whilst trying to fix the TV - Horace is only stunned.

In *Believe It or Not, Joe's Walking on Air Lois*, Bonnie and Bernice start visiting the Clam. This prompts Peter to construct the Quahog Men's Club in his back yard, only to have the women crash their party there too.

It happened on Peter's boat

Peter: Hey hey I got an idea. Lets play 'I Never.' You gotta drink if you did the thing that the person says they never did.

Cleveland: Oh I got one. I never slept with a woman with the lights on.

(They all drink.)

Joe: I'll go next, uh I never had sex with Cleveland's wife.

(Quagmire and Cleveland drink.)

Peter: Alright let's see uh. I never did a chick in a Logan airport bathroom.

(Only Quagmire drinks.)

(Later) Peter: God lets see what else is there um...I never gave a reach-around to a spider monkey while reciting the Pledge of Allegiance.

Quagmire: Oh God.

(Quagmire takes a drink.)

Joe: I uh I never picked up an illegal alien at Home Depot to take home and choke me while I touch myself.

Quagmire: Oh come on!

(Quagmire drinks again.)

Peter: Uh, I never did the same thing but with someone from Jo-Ann Fabrics.

Quagmire: Oh God this is ridiculous. (Drinks more and passes out.)

It happened at the Quahog Men's Club

Glenn: Would you have sex with Cleveland if it meant you could have sex with Angelina Jolie?

Peter: Griffin: Uh... yeah, yeah, I'd probably do it.

Glenn: Hang on, hang on... Missionary, and you have to look him in the eye. No closing your eyes and pretending it's somebody else. [Cleveland looks at Peter]

Peter: [pause] I think still yes.

Cleveland: Thank you, Peter.

Glenn: All right, here's another one. Who would you rather have sex with: a very pregnant Gina Gershon or Jenny McCarthy after a car accident?

Peter: W-wait. h-hang on. hang on. Look, you know-you know, I-I know this is a men's club, but why does it always have to be about sex? Like, okay, look– h-how about this? How about this? Who would you rather start a small business with: Janet Reno after a safari, or the fat guy from My Name Is Earl?

Glenn: That still sounds like a sex question.

Peter: It is not.

Glenn: Well then, what the hell does 'safari' have to do with it?

Cleveland: What's the guy from Earl's credit rating?

Peter: 651.

Cleveland: That's not bad.

Joe: Better than mine.

Cleveland: Does he have an idea. or do I have to come up with it myself?

Peter: He's got an idea, but it's not quite there.

Glenn: I'd have to give it to Janet Reno, 'cause I've always had this business plan for home delivery of prescription medications, and that–that seems like it's more her market.

Joe: This is stupid! I want to talk about vaginas.

Peter Griffin 101

"ARE YOU GONNA EAT THAT STAPLER?"

Peter Griffin is the star of the show. A man of the people. A man for all seasons. A man amongst men. A man barely alive. We cannot rebuild him. We don't have the technology.

Effluent? Yes. Affluent. No. Peter's farts are so noxious, so devilishly wallpaper-removing he once made himself pass out by farting in an airtight box.

The fat man, as Stewie calls him, is of Irish descent. He plays the tin whistle and makes statues of snakes made from potatoes.

Ever noticed how impulsive Peter can be? He once tried to molest Meg just to adopt a redneck lifestyle... and jealous? He once punched a whale that kissed Lois at Seaworld.

Rock 'n' roller, Peter Griffin is totally into KISS.

FUN FACTS

Peter once worked as a Fisherman on his own boat. It was called the 'S.S. More Powerful than Superman, Batman, Spider-Man and The Incredible Hulk Put Together.'

....

Peter is a committed drinker, addicted to cheap television, impulsive, thoughtless, and reckless. Just don't you call him feckless; he won't understand you and may think it's another name for a transvestite.

....

Peter was born in a Mexican hospital when his mother, Thelma, went to Mexico to have an abortion. However, Thelma went into labour during the procedure and both had to be smuggled back home to Providence.

....

In *Peter's Two Dads*, Peter discovers his biological father is Irishman Mickey McFinnigan. When Peter goes to visit McFinnegan, his father ignores him at first. The only thing left is to earn his respect by beating McFinnegan in a 'game of drink'.

All About Peter

You need to know all there is to know about Peter Griffin? Well, let's start at the beginning... Peter Griffin's ancestry is more patchwork quilt than rich tapestry. His ancestors include Moses Griffin, who led the Jews out of Egypt, Great Grandfather Willy 'Black-Eyed' Griffin, a Twenties silent film star, there's Peter Hitler, Adolf Hitler's flamboyant brother and Nate Griffin, an African American slave from Virginia, owned by Lois' ancestors.

However, the man that stands before you today is a self-made man. He's been an assembly worker at Happy-Go-Lucky toy factory, a private fisherman,

maid, nanny, bartender, Mayor, theatre producer/director, school board president, reality undercover drug investigator show actor, Petorian president, tobacco lobbyist, renaissance fair jouster, Bumblescum sheriff, TV producer, Church of The Fonz priest, Sumo wrestler, Erotic book author, Channel 5 News special reporter, Policeman, restaurant owner, football player, Christina Aguilera's manager, Carter Pewterschmidt's servant, buttscratcher salesman and even played Death.

We say Peter is a self-made man – it may be more true than any of us know. He might be a woman, he might have been made from a dustbin, a plunger, or a rake and a magnifying glass – like the Six Million Dollar man. In fact, in the episode *Running Mates*, Peter is a paradoy of the Six Million Dollar Man with a broom and a garbage can for legs!

Peter Griffin is a jealous guy. Not in a Brian Ferry way – he doesn't sound like he's been in a motor accident. Peter once punched his own reflection in a mirror after Lois described him as handsome. Peter Griffin is a stupid guy. He tried Hinduism but was kicked out after tackling the Hindu leader to the floor thinking the red dot on his head was a sniper rifle's laser target. But you know, most of all, Peter Griffin is a Family Guy.

FACTFILE

AGE:	42
PLACE OF BIRTH:	Mexico
BIRTH NAME:	Peter Löwenbräu Griffin
GENDER:	All Man, Baby. All Man.

101

Lois Griffin 101

"NOW THAT HER KIDS ARE OUT OF THE HOUSE, AT LEAST SHARON OSBOURNE HAS TIME TO RAISE OZZY."

Lois was born into a wealthy German American family, The Pewterschmidts. She met her Peter when he was a towel boy at the family country club. Lois found his lower-class, easy-going stupidity alluring, compared to the stuffy, uptight guys in her social circle. Stuffier than a posh teddy bear.

Once, Joe fell out of his chair and was about to fall into a sewer but Lois caught him. Lois shouted: "I can't hold on much longer!" Joe replied: "Lois, pretend I'm one of your children!" When he started to slip, he shouted: "Not Meg!"

International fame and fortune awaited Lois after she was crowned Miss Teen Rhode Island, but her father thought that the profession was beneath the dignity of the family, like being a politician.

She has a brain tumour, as revealed in *Petarded,* caused by repressing the fact that her husband is a moron.

FUN FACTS

All About Lois

The most important thing about Lois? She loves sex. Lois has slept with J. Geils, Daryl Hall, the pyro guy from the band Whitesnake, and Gene Simmons of KISS. She's bedded Bill Clinton (as has Peter) and Jerome – "I mean, me and Jerome dated 12 inches ago! Did I say inches?"

It's surprising that Lois let's anyone near her. For the birth of Meg, Lois went to get an abortion with Peter, but since the abortion doctor only had one arm, they decided against it. Chris was so big he was christened Elephant Child while Stewie left a 'ticking time bomb' in Lois' uterus!

Whatever you say about the woman, Lois has a certain sexy way about her – Quagmire, Brian, Chris and even Meg have all 'fessed up about wanting a tasty piece of Lois pie. Maybe they wouldn't be quite so turned on if they saw Lois in her childhood days. Lois used to be a circus freak, a dwarf-like thing who bounced up and down shouting 'Me likey bouncy!'

Lois is also a committed family girl. A family girl who is fiercely protective of her children... "I'm like one of those bald eagles on the discovery channel. Beautiful to look at, but mess with one of my chicks and I'll use my razor sharp talons to rip your eyes out."

Lois almost always acts heterosexual, but she does like girls. No, she really likes girls.

In *Brian Sings and Swings*, Lois shares a kiss with one of Meg's lesbian friends to teach Meg how to kiss. In *Stewie B. Goode*, Lois says: "Women are such teases, that's why I went back to men!"

In *Fifteen Minutes of Shame* she tells Meg's slumber party that she used to practice French kissing with her friends; and in *Stew-Roids* she lustfully rubs sunscreen on Bonnie's lower back.

FACTFILE

AGE:	42
PLACE OF BIRTH:	Newport, Rhode Island
BIRTH NAME:	Lois Pewterschmidt
GENDER:	More woman than Aphrodite

101

Chris Griffin 101

"WHAT DOES IT MEAN WHEN YOUR ARMPITS CRY STINKY TEARS?"

Cannabis? When it comes to life's gene pool, Chris might be the sort of kid who's in danger of drowning, but ask him why marijuana is legal and he's more lucid: "Pot is illegal because William Randolph Hearst had a smear campaign against marijuana in the 1930s to protect his interests in the timber industry because hemp was poised to replace wood as an inexpensive raw material for the manufacture of paper."

Herbert, Spooner Street's friendly paedophile, thinks that Chris is just about the sweetest kid you could ever force into a tight-fitting sailor suit.

Road to the Multiverse sees Chris win a gay man! He wants to keep him but Lois is sceptical... "A winner! Congratulations, son, you won a genuine living live homosexual." Homosexual: "Ooh, where are we going. Wait don't tell me." Chris: "Oh, boy. Mom can I keep him?" Lois: "Well it's a big responsibility, Chris. That means you'll have to clean up after him and feed him." Chris: "What do you eat?" Homosexual: "Attention." Chris: "I like your hair." Homosexual: "Still hungry!" Chris: "You have a beautiful speaking voice." Homosexual: "I'm full."

In Season Six's *Petarded* after Peter wins a game of Trivial Pursuit, Chris tells Meg: "My dad is smarter than your dad", to which Meg replies: "We have the same dad, idiot!" Chris responds: "Yeah, but mine's smarter!"

Says here that Chris wouldn't hurt a fly. Unless it landed on a hot dog.

All About Chris

Despite that enormous penis, Chris is not fantastic around girls. He once developed a crush on a girl, Anna. At their first date he told her: "You know Anna, when I first saw you, I thought you were the most beautiful girl in the world. And now, all I wanna do is show you my innermost self, but I'm afraid you'll reject me because you won't like what you see. Or, that you'll see my scrotum and see that it has a seam on it and then you'll think I'm made up of two different guys that were sewn together, 'cause that's what I think happened... I'm sorry. When I'm around a pretty girl, I get all worked up like a kid watching a toy commercial."

FUN FACTS

Chris believes his low grades in mathematics were self-inflicted after tickling his brain by sticking an army man's rifle up his nose and accidentally puncturing a lobe.

....

Chris can fit into any surrounding effortlessly. When, in *Patriot Games*, the family moved to London, England, Chris was able to quickly learn and speak Cockney.

....

One time, Peter slapped Chris on the back of the head and Chris shouted "HEY!". Peter pointed to a nearby floorlamp and Chris started fighting with it. Okay, he's not that bright, but he's got some great hidden talents.

In fact, Chris has a bigger tail than Peter. When Chris and Peter are in a sauna, Peter asks Chris what's wrong with his leg, only to say: "Oh my God that's not your leg!" Chris masturbates on Thursdays. That's a great day; enough time to recover your mojo before Friday night but you'll go in there nice and chill.

While he might not be that clued up about girls, when it comes to movies, the kid is in the picture.

101

FACTFILE

AGE:	15
PLACE OF BIRTH:	Quahog, Rhode Island
BIRTH NAME:	Christopher Cross Griffin
GENDER:	Longtail Elephant

Meg Griffin 101

"IF I DON'T GET MY DRIVER'S LICENCE, I'LL NEVER HAVE ANY BOYFRIENDS, I'LL NEVER GET MARRIED AND I'LL HAVE TO ADOPT A KID LIKE ROSIE O'DONNELL."

Meg rarely feels loved. Meg: "I just want to kill myself. I'm gonna go upstairs and eat a whole bowl of peanuts." Lois and Peter stare in silence. Meg: "I'm allergic to peanuts." Peter and Lois keep staring. Meg: "You don't know anything about me!" Peter: "Who was that guy?"

Ever wondered why Meg has identity issues? Her voice has been provided by five different people. Rachael MacFarlane, the younger sister of Seth, did the pilot; Lacey Chabert, who stars as Claudia Salinger in Party of Five, did the first season; Mila Kunis is the current voice and Tara Strong provides the singing voice. John Viener did the voice when she was 'Ron' in Stu & Stewie's Excellent Adventure.

Getting along with Chris isn't easy for Meg. She once told him: "Wow, Chris, did you lose weight?" He replied: "Well, I've been working out all week." Meg: "You look wicked skinny. I'm like, jealous." Chris: "Thanks, Meg. I'm jealous of your moustache."

FUN FACTS

When Lois tells Meg that eating to solve one's problems is no answer, Meg re-assures her: "I don't eat to solve my problems, I cut myself."

....

Meg strangles stray cats.

....

When Meg said she doesn't like it when Chris draws pictures of her head on a pig's body, he replied: "DON'T CENSOR ME!!!"

All About Meg

Megan Griffin is a freaky loser, and we don't mean like the girl with the flute in American Pie who pretends to be geeky but is actually Superhot. We know what we'd like to freakin' well do to her at Band Camp. And hey, isn't she also that girl from Buffy? Who also pretends to be geeky but then turns out to be like really dark and lesbian and stuff? S'pose it's like going on a date with a really great looking trans-sexual, hey Brian?

Back to Meg, which is probably facing the right way. Meg is largely ignored by her family. When Meg compared Lois' childhood bedroom to her own, her mother noted that they were exactly the same, apart from Lois' many trophies and pictures of friends.

Neither is she particularly lucky with men... one student fired a nail gun into his own stomach to avoid a date and another murdered his own brother to have an excuse not to go to prom (he had to attend his brother's funeral). Two other guys drenched themselves in gasoline, set themselves on fire and threw themselves out a window screaming in horror after simply looking at her.

Another time, she was taken hostage and asked: "So... is, uh, is this like the part where you guys have your way with me? You know, where I'm like helpless, and you guys take turns... you know?" The robber replied: "OH, NO! Oh, god! Oh, no, no no no no! Ewww!" She tried to re-assure them: "No seriously, I won't scream or anything."

Meg has to shave daily. As Stewie once so eloquently put it: "You ever seen a Blacksmith's apron?" And, Stewie once told Meg that while she sleeps he spits in her mouth. As Meg says: "Do you know what that feels like? To have a baby tell you he spits in your mouth?"

Meg has had some results – she did have a brief fling with Brian and admitted to being turned on by how flat and wide his tongue was.

FACTFILE

AGE:	17
PLACE OF BIRTH:	Quahog, Rhode Island
BIRTH NAME:	Megan Griffin
GENDER:	Girl (but not a sexy one)

101

Stewie Griffin 101

"OH, JUST A LITTLE SOMETHING I DO AROUND HERE ONCE A WEEK CALLED NAKED TEA PARTY. GOT MY TEACUP HERE, NOW ALL I NEED IS A TEABAG. THAT SOMETHING THAT INTERESTS YOU, MY FRIEND?"

Stewie's voice is based on that of oily British actor Rex Harrison, particularly in My Fair Lady.

The boy is constantly plotting ways to kill Lois, holding a grudge against her because of his nine-month stay in her ovarian Bastille.

Ever wondered who is truly Stewie's best friend? Brian? Stewie? Bertram? Karina? No, that honour would have to go to Rupert, his teddy bear.

When Stewie speaks, the world listens. But in an ongoing Family Guy joke, only Brian can understand Stewie. And sometimes Lois, and Jillian, Brian's girlfriend. And Peter once did? No sense.

In *Love Blactually*, Stewie wants to talk to Loretta. "Just let me do all the talking." says Stewie. Brian replies: "No, I think I can communicate with her better. She's only going to get the gist of what you're saying." Stewie: "Really? Isn't she one of those people outside the family who can understand me?" Brian: "No, I think because of Cleveland she's close enough to the main cast that it might be a little weird."

Email Stewie at loismustdie@yahoo.com

All About Stewie

Flamboyant, eccentric, equipped with a laser gun and a teddy bear, Stewie Griffin is a baby obsessed with world domination, matricide and Jolly Farm Revue.

Ambiguous of sexual orientation and the vocabulary of a young Will Self, Stewie often refers to his father Peter as 'The Fat Man', sharing his closest thoughts and secrets with only his close friend and confidant, Rupert.

Despite his diminutive size, Stewie is no stranger to theft, carjacking, loan sharking, forgery, and the most heinous murders. He is an angry, jealous little man who has mastered every science but has yet to conquer broccoli.

Stewie is often romantically involved with a bevy of baby beauties. He also enjoys the odd spanking from Lois, like in *Peter's Two Dads*. It is unknown whether the rest of the family can understand Stewie. The episodes *Stewie Kills Lois* and *Lois Kills Stewie* are the only ones where he is really spoken to properly by all family members, whereas the previous week Peter had ignored his macaroni picture of an owl.

Other than Lois, Stewie has many, many enemies. The Man in White who Stewie thought was supposed to return him to Lois' womb on his birthday was assassinated; there's Bertram his half brother and nemesis. Bertram often admits defeat by yelling "MOMMY!" Brad the fishboy who beat Stewie in the pool; Charlie the Bully stole his trike; Connie D'Amico who dumped him (he took revenge by framing her for paedophilia) and Olivia Fuller. Stewie locked Olivia in a cardboard house and set it on fire. Stewie don't take kindly to being wronged. Oooooooh nooooooooooooo.

FUN FACTS

In *Mr Griffin Goes To Washington*, the penny finally drops for Lois: "My god, it all makes sense now. My baby is some kind of diabolical genius bent on world domination!" Stewie: "Bravo, Lois. The last horse finally crosses the finish line." Lois: "Stewie! All these months I should've paid attention to what you've said. You're an evil child. Why, why did I have to go and smoke pot when I was pregnant with you?"

....

In *Quagmire's Baby*, Stewie made Bitch-Stewie, a mentally-challenged, deformed clone of himself who is made to serve his master and lives on a crude peanut paste. He says things like: "I did some poos, I did some poos. I didn't mean to." Which is funny, no matter how you cut it.

....

Wizard Magazine, which is for boys who don't shower or shave, voted Stewie 95th biggest villain of all time. You know who won? The Joker. The freakin' Joker?

FACTFILE

AGE:	1 (For eight seasons)
PLACE OF BIRTH:	Quahog, Rhode Island
BIRTH NAME:	Stewart Gilligan Griffin
GENDER:	Changeable

101

Brian Griffin 101

"GOSH, I'D LIKE TO HELP YOU, BUT I'VE GOT TO GO OUT IN THE HALL AND CHEW ON THE BACK OF MY ASS FOR ABOUT FIVE MINUTES."

Brian drives a 2004 Toyota Prius. It is seen in the episode *The Juice Is Loose* pulling up on the Griffins' driveway – the licence plate reads BRI-DOG and has a 'Kucinich 04' bumper sticker – Dennis Kucinich was a candidate for the Democratic Presidential nomination in '04 and '08, but you probably knew that, right?

Racist. There's no other way to say it (other than Republican), Brian is a racist. He gets it from his father. Like all good racists, Brian hides it well.

In *Brian Goes Back to College*, it is revealed that Brian went to Brown University in Rhode Island, but did not graduate. He is just one class short - Physics 101.

A man's best friend Brian might be, but he has to draw the line somewhere. When Peter built an indoor water slide by running water down the house stairs and injured himself, Brian told him: "I'm not going to take you to the hospital because if I do, you won't learn anything."

Never one to 'do' regular dogs, Brian was once accused of impregnating Carter Pewterschmidt's racing dog, Seabreeze. However, the father turned out to be Ted Turner.

FUN FACTS

Stewie travelled to the future and learned that Brian died from eating chocolate. When Stewie saw Brian dead, he called him a douchebag. though Future Stewie told Past Stewie that the meaning of the word changed after President Douchebag took office.

....

There's a clip in *Stewie Griffin: The Untold Story* which sees Brian in heaven playing cards with Vincent van Gogh, Kurt Cobain and Ernest Hemingway. When Brian asks how they all died, they reply that they killed themselves with great passion. He admits that he ate some chocolate out of the trash.

....

Brian likes the finer things in life - wine, women, jazz, a good smoke and throw-up. Yip, sure does like throw-up.

All About Brian

Brian's life has been pretty far from a bed of roses - his father, Coco, was run over by a milk truck and his mother, Biscuit, put him up for adoption - or rather put him in a cardboard box lined with a dirty towel. Brian returns to Texas to find out what happened to Biscuit and finds her stuffed, being used as a table.

Today, he's an eight-year-old walking, talking, white Labrador who likes eating trash, leaving dead birds lying around and running from the vacuum. Despite a racist streak, Brian

can speak French, Spanish and Tagalog. This could prove important because Brian might need the extra languages if he visits the Philippines, where they eat dogs.

S'pose he could avoid a peppercorn, Tabasco and bay leaf-based death by shouting: "makakuha ng isang buhay mo malungkot geek at hihinto sa check up ng mga pagsasalin!" What does it mean? Does it matter? It might give him time to make a quick escape!

A member of Mensa, Brian can also imitate a barbershop quartet without accompaniment. But his real passion? It's writing. His novel 'Faster Than the Speed of Love' made news as being the slowest-selling novel of all time. Apparently, it's based on the plot of Aces: Iron Eagle III. Which, we think we can agree, is some of Lou Gosset Jnr's best work.

Brian is a rationalist and is often critical of organised religion. When Francis Griffin physically threatens him, Brian sarcastically replies: "That's very Christian; believe what I say or I'll hurt you. Not all dogs go to Heaven." Brian almost definitely won't.

FACTFILE

AGE:	8 (That's 42 in dog years).
PLACE OF BIRTH:	Austin, Texas
ADOPTED NAME:	Brian Griffin
GENDER:	Labrador

101

FAMILY GUY'S Dirty Dozen

CAUTION
SPECIAL DAD

#12: Petarded
SEASON FOUR, EPISODE SIX

WHAT IS A DIRTY DOZEN? A US ARMY MAJOR ASSIGNED A DOZEN CONVICTED MURDERERS TO TRAIN AND LEAD THEM INTO A MASS ASSASSINATION MISSION OF GERMAN OFFICERS IN WORLD WAR II? NOPE. A DIRTY DOZEN IS WHEN ENGLISH SAILORS WAGER A NICKEL, A PICKLE AND A SICKLE THAT THEY CAN GO TWELVE WHOLE DAYS WITHOUT CHANGING THEIR UNDERWEAR.

Now, there's only one thing darker, more rancid and more terrifying than Peter's underwear drawer, and that's the on-going feud over Family Guy's most popular episode. Sure, we know that any episode where Meg actually speaks rules it out of the bidding, but other than that? We haven't got a clue! We looked high and wide, low and narrow and even rifled through our very own stack of Mexican pornography for a poll and discovered no help. But eventually we had to come up with these twelve crack episodes that we're calling the Dirty Dozen. Or, if you like, Family Guy's twelve dirty cracks.

PETER: DON'T SAY 'RETARD', CHRIS. WE PREFER TO BE CALLED 'LITTLE PEOPLE'.

#12

READ IT!

So Peter and Lois invite the neighbours over for Trivial Pursuit, right? To give Peter a chance, Lois gives him the pre-school questions.

Peter wins the game after being able to simply say the word 'what' and, of course, can't wait to bask in the glory. He just can't resist telling everyone: "Goodnight, losers!"

Like the dog that he truly is, Brian snaps. To prove Peter's lack of intelligence, he challenges Peter to apply for the MacArthur Genius Grant. When the results come back it turns out that Peter is actually mentally retarded.

After realising he is not a genius, Peter sinks into depression and, while driving home, runs over Tom Tucker. Tucker is furious, though seeing Peter is "that retarded fellow" he lets him go without calling the police. Hey Presto, Peter realises being mentally retarded means he can get away with anything he likes! Hilarity ensues. After other hi-jinks, Peter accidentally spills the contents of a deep fat fryer from a fast-food restaurant over Lois. With Lois in the hospital and thinking Peter is mentally unfit, the Child Protective Services take away the Griffin children, homing them with Cleveland.

Peter tries to get his children back by taking seven prostitutes into Cleveland's house, thinking it will show Cleveland is unfit to be a parent. The social worker sees through the plot and five of the prostitutes leave. Lois returns, saves the day, gets the kids back and will smell like French Fries for the next six months!

KNOW IT!

■ Peter's social worker Vern is "bent on diluting the already watered-down significance of the elevated hand slap" by high-fiving every one and every thing.

HEAR IT!

CHRIS: "My dad's smarter than your dad."
MEG: "We have the same dad, idiot!"
CHRIS: "Yeah, but mine's smarter!"

LOIS GRIFFIN: "Peter, mental retardation usually happens before you're born. It isn't something you can catch. Don't you think you're overreacting?"
PETER: "Well, excuse me for being retarded!"

BRIAN: "Do you ever stop and think 'Wow, I'm married to that guy'?"
LOIS: "Nah, I just repress it."

FAMILY GUY'S Dirty Dozen

#11: Da Boom
SEASON TWO, EPISODE THREE

IT'S THE END OF THE WORLD! BUT THEY WILL BE FINE! THIS IS HOW THE GRIFFINS SURVIVE A NUCLEAR HOLOCAUST – WELL, SORT OF SURVIVE! TALES OF MUTANTS, PLUMBING, EGG-LAYING AND MASS SLAUGHTER. BUT IS IT ALL FOR REAL?

CLEVELAND: GUNS ONLY LEAD TO TROUBLE.

PETER: RIGHT. NOW WHEN THAT TROUBLE HAPPENS, WE'LL BE READY TO BLOW ITS FREAKIN' HEAD OFF.

READ IT!

On the final day of the last millennium, a costumed man warns Peter that the world is going to end... Peter, being a caring father and a man who also puts his family first, especially if he were to ever to face a masked gunman, locks them up in a bomb shelter to avoid the nuclear holocaust.

At the stroke of midnight a nuclear holocaust flattens Quahog, mutating those outside the Griffins' bunker. Cleveland and Quagmire are fused together to make Clevemire or Quagland – part sex maniac, part token black guy.

When food runs out, the family travels to Natick, Massachusetts, to find what they hope will be the last surviving Twinkie factory. On the way, Stewie is exposed to toxic waste and begins to mutate into.... an octopus. Believing they can survive on this newfound food source, they decide to set up New Quahog and Peter becomes their leader (due to the fact that it was his idea to search out the factory) beginning his inevitable decline into ill-judgment. Peter gives the citizens careers by having them draw one out of a hat and tears out the town's plumbing pipes to make guns.

Stewie the octopus begins laying eggs while Peter is kicked out of town for his ill-stewardship. As the townspeople throw their last gun onto the pile, hundreds of newly spawned Stewie octopi hatch and destroy the city. The townspeople are unable to protect themselves, if only they'd understood the vision of the great man, Peter Griffin. What need have we for water if we have no guns?

And it was all a dream... The episode ends with Bobby and Pam Ewing from the TV series Dallas, in a parody of the famous shower scene, where an entire previous season of the series was revealed as a dream.

KNOW IT!

■ In this episode, Lacey Chabert, the chick in Lost In Space with the American teeth, was supposed to voice Meg Griffin. Instead, for the first time, Meg was voiced by Mila Kunis, the Russian chick with the American teeth.

■ This is the first time Peter fights The Giant Chicken.

■ When this exchange takes place, it's a reference to the film, Alien. Meg: "There's no factory?" Stewie: "Ahh, oh very good fat man, we've followed the pied piper of Hamsteak to the gates of oblivion and look what it's brought us! We're finished, we're done, game over man game over. Ah, damn it!"

HEAR IT!

WHEN QUAGLAND TELLS LOIS THAT THEY'RE HUNGRY, SHE REMINISCES AND REGRETS ABOUT HOW MUCH FOOD THEY'VE WASTED IN THE GRIFFIN HOUSEHOLD. CUT TO PETER TRYING TO FEED MAGNUM PI THROUGH THE TV SCREEN!

PETER: "Here, Tom Selleck. Come on. Down the hatch. Come on. Hey HEY! None for you, Higgins! Trying to steal Tom Selleck's food! No. No! You've had yours!"

LOIS: "Peter, what are you doin'? You just ate a year's worth of food!"

(PETER HAS JUST EATEN ALL THE DEHYDRATED FOOD RATIONS)

PETER: "Huh. What a waste of money. I'm still hungry."

(PETER DRINKS A GLASS OF WATER, THEN IMMEDIATELY BALLOONS TO SEVERAL TIMES HIS SIZE)

PETER: "Everyone leave. I have to poop. NOW!"

#11

FAMILY GUY'S Dirty Dozen

#10: To Love and Die In Dixie

SEASON THREE, EPISODE TWELVE

DEEP DOWN SOUTH - AND THIS HAS NOTHING TO DO WITH FRIED CHICKEN - THE GRIFFINS ARE FORCED INTO HIDING WHEN THEIR LIVES COME UNDER THREAT. THE HILL BILLYS ARE HERE - AND SO IS A WHOLE NEW MESS FOR THE DYSFUNCTIONAL FAMILY!

MEG: THIS IS OUR HOUSE?
LOIS: OH COME ON MEG, I BET IF WE FIXED IT UP A LITTLE BIT, IT COULD BE A PIECE OF CRAP.

READ IT!

Chris needs a little extra, and we're not talking about the contents of Herbert's dressing gown. He needs money to pay for a birthday gift for a girl and takes up a newspaper round. He witnesses a robbery at a store and his bike is stolen by the burglar as a getaway vehicle. Chris identifies the thief out of a police line-up before Peter shows up and tells the thief that he's here to pick up Chris who was going to "finger the guy who held up that convenience store".

Peter gives the crim a picture of Chris, a list of his school schedule… and his greatest fears. When the thief escapes prison, he swears to get Chris, which means the Griffins are placed in the Witness Protection Program in Bumblescum, the Deep South. And when we say deep, we don't mean intellectually.

Peter and Brian become the local law enforcement – think Starsky and Hutch with a beer gut and the ability to lick their own testicles. Incredibly, Meg finds herself the most popular girl in school, and Chris finds himself feeling stirrings of love for his new friend Sam. Stewie joins a Hill Billy jug band.

Chris thinks Sam is a boy but kind of likes it when they kiss. When the two meet again, Chris tells Sam he wants to be a friend, not a lover.

While swimming, Sam is revealed to be a girl. Chris feels awkward. At the hootenanny (or hoedown), Chris explains to Sam that he had no problem talking to her when he thought she was a guy. So she tells Chris to think of her as a boy and then they can go make out. The criminal tracks the Griffins down and attempts to kill both Chris and Sam. The criminal is shot by Sam's father - good 'Ol Deep South ad hoc justice.

KNOW IT!

■ Fleckenstein, which Peter pitches in a potential song title to Simon and Garfunkel, is the name of one of the Family Guy writing assistants, Matt Fleckenstein.

■ Waylon Jennings, who served as the narrator on the original *The Dukes of Hazzard*, provided the voiceover on this episode.

■ When Stewie shouts "I got blisters on me fingers!" it is a reference to the Beatles song *Helter Skelter*.

■ This is the first episode in which we meet Herbert.

HEAR IT!

PETER: "I dunno, Brian, maybe Lois is right. Maybe it is time for me to get a job."
BRIAN: "Yeah, too bad you always blow it in the interview."
(PETER AT A JOB INTERVIEW)
INTERVIEWER: "So, Peter, where do you see yourself in five years?"
PETER: (thinks… don't say doing your wife, don't say doing your wife, don't say doing your wife.)
PETER: "Doing your…" (sees a picture of the interviewer's son)
PETER: "Son?"

THE GRIFFIN'S ANSWER MACHINE: "You have 113 new messages."
BEEP!
LOIS GRIFFIN: "Oh my!"
HERBERT: "Uh, yeah, I was just wonderin', uh… mhm..where the newspaper boy was."
BEEP!
HERBERT: "Haven't seen the newspaper in a couple days. Wonderin' if he ever gon' come back."
BEEP!
HERBERT: "Guess whooooo? Sorry to leave you so many messages. Just lonely here. Thinkin' about the muscly-armed paperboy. Wishin' he'd come by and bring me some good news."
BEEP!
HERBERT: "Where are ya?"
BEEP!
HERBERT: "Ah, you're startin' to piss me off, you little piggly sumbitch. Call me."

#10

SAY WHAT Peter?

The world and life, according to Peter. The great (and we mean that in the largest form possible) man admits he doesn't even know what he is talking about, but still gives us his thoughts on everything from fake moon landings, women being from Venus, dodgy neighbours and dogs laying eggs...

★ ★ ★ ★ ★

I want everyone to call me by my Hebrew name: Gggwggwg...

LOIS, MY PENIS BELONGS ON STAGE!

Lois, brothers and sisters fighting is as natural as a white man's dialogue in a Spike Lee movie.

PICTURES SPEAK LOUDER THAN WORDS. BECAUSE SOME WORDS ARE BIG AND HARD TO UNDERSTAND.

How many monkeys does it take to screw in a light bulb? Three – one to screw it in and two to throw feces at each other.

HERE'S TO OUR NEIGHBOURS. THEY MAY BE BLACK, HANDICAPPED OR A HEARTLESS SEX HOUND, BUT IF IT WEREN'T FOR THEM, SOME SMELLY HAWAIIANS MIGHT MOVE IN.

Your aunt Marguerite is probably laughing at me while she's burning in hell, may she rest in peace.

I FEEL TERRIBLE BRIAN, I PUT LOIS IN A HOSPITAL AND I LOST THE KIDS. THIS IS TURNING OUT WORSE THAN STEWIE'S IPOD COMMERCIAL.

★ ★ ★ ★ ★

I'M JUST A BIG FAKE, LIKE THE MOON LANDING AND MARKY MARK'S HOG IN BOOGIE NIGHTS

★ ★ ★ ★ ★

My name is Peter Griffin... my friends call me Peter for short.

BRIAN, IT'S MOMENTS LIKE THIS THAT MAKE ME SAD YOU'RE GONNA DIE FIFTY YEARS BEFORE I DO.

Wait, wait, wait, wait a second. You're tellin' me that I came all the way to Kentucky to get some of your fried chicken, and the Colonel isn't even workin' today?!?

DON'T WORRY, I'VE GOT AN IDEA-AN IDEA SO SMART MY HEAD WOULD EXPLODE IF I EVEN BEGAN TO KNOW WHAT I WAS TALKING ABOUT.

GUYS, OUR MONEY PROBLEMS ARE OVER; WE'RE OFFICIALLY ON WELFARE! COME ON, KIDS, HELP ME SCATTER CAR PARTS ON THE FRONT LAWN.

At least they don't put their feminine ointments next to the mustard, Lois. That was the worst hot dog I ever ate.

LISTEN CHRIS, I READ A BOOK SAYING THAT WOMEN ARE FROM VENUS, ALL RIGHT SO HERE'S WHAT YOU GET HER. THICK LAYERS OF SULPHURIC ACID, VISCOUS SURFACE ROCK, AND CORONETS WHICH SEEM TO BE COLLAPSED DOMES OF A LARGE MAGMA CHAMBER. HERE'S FIVE DOLLARS.

I am so not competitive. In fact, I am the least non-competitive. So I win.

THE TWO OF YOU WILL ONE DAY BLESS OUR HOME WITH THE PITTER PATTER OF SWEET LITTLE GRANDCHILDREN AS UGLY AS SIN.

Hey, where is that Peter Griffin? He told me he'd give me a hundred dollars if I took off all my clothes.

HUH, YOU KNOW SOMETHING? I ALWAYS THOUGHT THAT DOGS LAID EGGS. SO, YEAH. I LEARNED SOMETHING TODAY.

WOMEN ARE NOT PEOPLE, THEY ARE DEVICES BUILT BY OUR LORD JESUS CHRIST FOR OUR ENTERTAINMENT.

THIS IS GREAT. NOT ONLY DID I LIVE LONG ENOUGH TO SEE MEG GO TO HER FIRST DANCE BUT I'M TAKING HER TOO. THANKS, GERITOL

You ever watch that show Scrubs? Lois had it on the other night, and I was kinda fading in and out, you know. I was watching and wondering..... which one is the funny guy?

GIVING A SPEECH RUNNING FOR THE SCHOOL BOARD: THIS IS LIFE SO GO AND HAVE A BALL. BECAUSE THE WORLD DON'T MOVE TO THE BEAT OF JUST ONE DRUM. WHAT MIGHT BE RIGHT FOR YOU MAY NOT BE RIGHT FOR SOME. YOU TAKE THE GOOD, YOU TAKE THE BAD, YOU TAKE THEM BOTH AND THERE YOU HAVE ... MY OPENING STATEMENT. SIT, UBU, SIT. GOOD DOG.

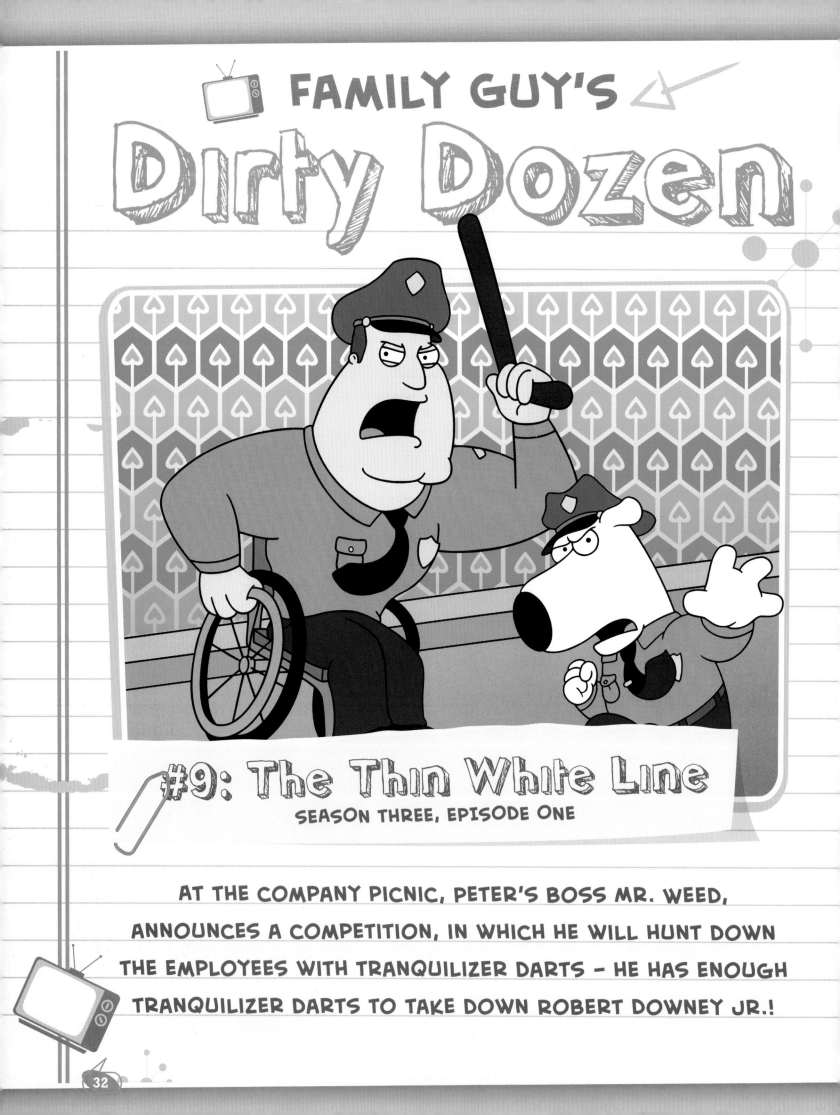

FAMILY GUY'S Dirty Dozen

#9: The Thin White Line
SEASON THREE, EPISODE ONE

AT THE COMPANY PICNIC, PETER'S BOSS MR. WEED, ANNOUNCES A COMPETITION, IN WHICH HE WILL HUNT DOWN THE EMPLOYEES WITH TRANQUILIZER DARTS – HE HAS ENOUGH TRANQUILIZER DARTS TO TAKE DOWN ROBERT DOWNEY JR.!

BRIAN: SO I SEE YOU GOT A NEW RECEPTIONIST. NICE LITTLE BODY ON HER, HUH?

THERAPIST: THAT'S MY DAUGHTER.

BRIAN: WELL, WE COULD PROBABLY CALL THIS AN EARLY DAY, HUH?

READ IT!

Brian tells his therapist that he's trapped in his own life. The Doc suggest Brian should do some charity work and get outside his own life.

At the company picnic, Peter's boss Mr. Weed, announces a competition, in which he will hunt down the employees with tranquilizer darts.

After being shot multiple times, Peter is the only one still conscious and wins a cruise vacation.

A charitable, but downbeat, Brian is returning home after almost killing an old woman at the hospital.

He tells Joe what Bonnie's been cooking from three nights ago so Joe offers him a job as a drug sniffing dog with the police.

At the airport, Brian sniffs out a bystander who is secretly carrying cocaine. Brian accidentally inhales the cocaine and becomes addicted but not before he busts a filthy group of drug peddling midgets.

Brian's addiction grows worse and, after attacking an innocent man, he is kicked off the police force. After a night with a hooker, the Griffins and Brian's psychiatrist insist he goes to rehab.

Missing out on the vacation, Peter decides to join Brian at the rehab centre. While there, Peter causes premature births in pregnant teens and gives drugs to patients in exchange for food.

The counsellor tells Brian that Peter is his real problem, the underlying reason behind his addiction. Man's best friend doesn't take the news well and defends Peter.

Brian decides it's time to leave Quahog and move to California to live with his cousin, Jasper, setting up the episode *Brian Does Hollywood* where Brian decides to become a film maker.

KNOW IT!

■ The music played when Brian catches his first drug dealer is taken from the iconic cop show CHiPS starring Erik Estrada.

■ The sign in front of the rehab clinic reads: 'Providence Rehab Clinic - Because, dude, it's time.'

HEAR IT!

BRIAN TAKES A BLIND MAN INTO CINEMA TO SEE THE BLAIR WITCH PROJECT, IN WHICH BRIAN SAYS: "Ok they're in the woods. The camera keeps on moving. Uh, I think they're looking for something, I don't know, I wasn't listening. Nothing's happening... nothing's happening... something about a map. Nothing's happening... it's over. A lot of people in the audience look pissed."

#9

33

FAMILY GUY'S
Dirty Dozen

#8: Death Is A Bitch
SEASON TWO, EPISODE SIX

IN WHICH PETER DISCOVERS HE IS A
BIG FAT LUMP... AND DEATH KNOCKS
ON THE DOOR. BUT DEATH IS DEAD.
NOT WITH US? DON'T WORRY, READ
THE WHOLE STORY, AND NOTHING
WILL BECOME MUCH CLEARER...

DEATH: I'M CALISTA FLOCKHART: WHO DO YOU THINK I AM? I'M DEATH.

#8

READ IT!

Lois finds a lump on Peter's chest. She worries the lump could be cancer. Peter sees a doctor. Before his tests return, Peter pretends he is dying, setting up a yard sale for life insurance and trying to buy himself a coffin.

Turns out the lump is just a fatty lump. Peter does not want to pay the hospital bill so declares himself dead.

Death shows up at Peter's house. Despite Lois' protests, Peter decides he should, really, accompany Death to wherever he lives. However, Peter decide to make one last break for it and runs away, Death pursues him and, while attempting to catch Peter, sprains his ankle. Don't mock sprained ankles; they are the Vesuvius of minor injuries.

Death stays at the Griffins' house while his ankle heals. While Death recovers no-one can die. So Peter bets that he can jump from tall buildings, drink 300 beers and make fun of the toughest people at the bar, all without dying. The bar

gets annoyed and repeatedly shoots Peter. Peter doesn't die. A stray bullet hits Cleveland but he doesn't die. The bar starts shooting each other and laughs upon discovering that they're still alive. Meanwhile, Stewie tries to kill Lois and, failing, realises he needs Death healthy.

The fact that no one can die becomes top news. Death is outraged but, instead of punishing Peter by killing him, Death allows Peter to redeem himself by having him take over Death's job in order to prove to people they can still die.

Peter is charged with killing the kids from Dawson's Creek who are on a crowded passenger plane. Instead, Peter unwittingly kills two airplane pilots, proving people are not immortal, and forcing actress Karen Black to land the plane. The Griffins and Death part on good terms.

KNOW IT!

- Stewie's e-mail address is revealed as loismustdie@yahoo.com

- This is the only time where Death is voiced by Norm MacDonald. In all subsequent appearances, Death is voiced by Adam Carolla. Carolla is the boxer in 'The Hammer', which ain't bad. It just ain't knockout. Heh, heh. Knockout, geddit?

HEAR IT!

DR. HARTMAN: "This doesn't look very good. No, this doesn't look very good at all..."
LOIS: "Oh!"
DR. HARTMAN: (shows a child-like drawing of himself) "My Nephew drew my portrait; it doesn't look a thing like me. I mean, look at the nose, it's all..."
LOIS: "Will you just tell us about Peter's tests?"
DR. HARTMAN: "Okay, okay. Mr. Griffin, all your tests came back negative. As it turns out the lump on your chest was just a fatty corpuscle."
PETER: "Fatty corpuscle? Wait a minute, how the hell can a dead comedian from the silent movie era be lodged in my left bosom?"

HITLER: "Today on Hitler ve vill be talking vit Hollywood hunk Christian Slater."
HITLER: "Now, so tell me. In your next movie. Ve get to see your butt?"
SLATER: "Yes, yes you do."
HITLER: "Can ve see it right now?"
SLATER: "Um? Well, uh, alright Hitler."
HITLER: "Oh, Oh, he's going to do it!"
HITLER: "If you're going to be in the Los Angeles area and vud like tickets to Hitler zen call 213-Du Werdest Eine Krankenschwester Brauchen!"

FAMILY GUY'S Dirty Dozen

#7: E. Peterbus Unum
SEASON TWO, EPISODE 18

THINGS ARE GOING SWIMMINGLY UNTIL PETER PLANS TO SPLASH OUT ON A POOL. AND THAT'S WHEN EVERYONE GETS A SINKING FEELING, A STATE OF INDEPENDENCE IS DECLARED AND THE ARMY AND DIPLOMATS GET INVOLVED...

#7

Chabert who voiced Meg Griffin in Season One and some of Season Two was a regular cast member on Party of Five.

■ When Mayor West is showing Peter that his home is not on the map and it zooms into a close-up of the map, you can see the names of different streets, one of them is called 'McFar Lane' in reference to Seth MacFarlane.

■ The title is based on the United States' motto found on the Great Seal, 'E. pluribus unum', Latin for 'Out of many, one'.

CHRIS: DAD, I TRIED TO GO TO SCHOOL BUT THIS GUY WON'T LET ME.

PETER: OH YEAH? HIM AND WHAT ARMY?

CHRIS: THE U.S. ARMY. (POINTS TO SOLDIERS IN STREET)

PETER: OH, THAT'S A GOOD ARMY.

READ IT!

Peter's plans to build a swimming pool in his backyard are derailed when a request for a permit reveals Peter's house is not even in the U S of A.

Peter declares his house to be the new micro-nation of Petoria! Peter was going to call it Peterland but there's already a gay bar down by the airport called that.

Peter, as the new President of Petoria, goes on a cross-border tirade violating important laws on stepping on grass, littering and vandalism and trivial sexual harassment laws. Even worse, he insults bartender Horace at The Drunken Clam and brings beer out into the streets.

Snubbed at the UN, Peter follows an Iraq diplomat's advice and annexes Joe's pool, calling it 'Joe-hio'.

Chris can't get to school because the US Army surrounds and blockades Petoria as part of 'Operation: Desert Clam'. Petoria's electricity and water is cut and Lois homeschools her children. Peter refuses to return Joe's pool, but after Lois catches Stewie mixing with the foreign leaders, it leads to her taking the kids and leaving Peter, who bravely surrenders. Grateful to Peter, Lois promises to scratch his back with a matchbook cover every night. In the end, all the events of the episode turn out to have been filmed and are used in social studies classes 200 years in the future.

KNOW IT!

■ Peter mentions that he can't get over Party of Five being cancelled. Party of Five was scheduled to be cancelled after the first season but, due to a fan campaign (like Family Guy), a second season was eventually made. Lacey

HEAR IT!

AFTER PETER CUT THE SPOONER STREET ELECTRICITY OFF THE ELECTRICIAN COMES TO REPAIR IT

ELECTRICIAN: "Well, I fixed the powerline, but the town's zoning laws prohibit building a pool back there."

PETER: "What are you talking about? It's my yard!"

ELECTRICIAN: "I'm sorry but your house is too close to the curb."

PETER: "Oh Yeah? Well your eyes are too close to your nose!"

ELECTRICIAN: "That may be, but you know what? I only have to wear one goggle when I go swimming in my pool!"

PETER: "Ey, way wait! Come back here!"

ELECTRICIAN: "What?"

PETER: "...I have to draw you."

(IN A BEDROOM, WHERE THE ELECTRICIAN IS LAYING NAKED ON THE BED WHILE PETER IS PAINTING HIM.)

PETER: "You're why cavemen painted on walls!"

She looks like butter wouldn't melt in her mouth but don't judge Lois on looks alone! This woman could cause a meltdown with some of her beliefs and thoughts so best not let her chat for too long! Mind you, Peter's already had his say so stand aside and give the woman in his life a bit of space...

CHRIS YOU CAN'T JOIN THE ARMY! BESIDES, THE ARMY'S WEAK. NOW THE MARINES! THOSE ARE THE MEN YOU WANNA HAVE.

OK Chris. Now that we have practiced kissing and cuddling, we'll practice eating out... at a fancy restaurant.

I'VE SEEN THAT CRAPPY JULIA ROBERTS MOVIE FORTY-SEVEN TIMES. HAVE YOU SEEN THE LIPS ON THAT WOMAN? LIKE A BABOON'S ASS ON HER FACE.

MY DAYS IN COLLEGE WERE SO EXCITING. THIS ONE TIME, THE NATIONAL GUARD CAME AND SHOT SOME OF MY FRIENDS.

PETER, I GOT A WAX JOB AND LET'S JUST SAY YOU'RE CLEARED FOR LANDING!

AND TO THINK, BRIAN, I WAS LIKE A DAY AWAY FROM HAVING SEX WITH YOU. I WAS GONNA PUSH THOSE BEDS TOGETHER AND TAKE YOU AROUND THE FREAKIN' WORLD, BRIAN! BUT A NICE PAT ON THE HEAD IS JUST AS GOOD, HUH? YOU WANT YOUR BALL? YOU WANT YOUR BALL?

Women are such teases. That's why I went back to men.

I'M JUST GONNA ASSUME THAT 'LESS TALKIE MORE FETCHIE' IS CHINESE FOR 'I LOVE YOU.'

ARE YOU KATE MOSS? FOR SOMEONE WITH NO BREASTS, YOU'VE DONE VERY WELL FOR YOURSELF. GOOD FOR YOU.

MY DAUGHTER NEEDS A MAKEOVER LIKE THERE'S NO FRICKING TOMORROW.

KIDS, YOUR GRANDFATHER'S EARS ARE NOT GROSS AND THEY ARE CERTAINLY NOT AN ENCHANTED FOREST.

Oh, that's it. Peter is completely out of control. We've got to do something to take him down and get your company back. In order to oust an idiot, we've got to think like an idiot. Let's see. What's Peter's weakness. He's got to have a weakness. Swamp monsters, of course!

BECAUSE MEG, ESTELLE TOLD ME THAT SOMEONE IN THE FAMILY WAS IN DANGER OF DROWNING, AND THAT I SHOULD TAKE SOME STEPS TO PREVENT IT. SO, FROM NOW ON, EVERYBODY HAS A BATH BUDDY.

BRIAN, YOUR SCRIPT? IT WAS ENCHANTING. THIS BRIAN GRIFFIN – I'VE NEVER MET THIS BRIAN GRIFFIN. I WOULD HAVE TOLD YOU LAST NIGHT, BUT I WAS 100% SURE YOU RIPPED IT OFF. BUT AFTER SPENDING THE LAST 18 HOURS ON THE INTERNET AND IN LIBRARIES TRYING TO FIND TRACES OF IT SOMEWHERE, I COULDN'T FIND A THING.

★ ★ ★ ★ ★

CLEVELAND, DON'T YOU SEE THIS IS WHY YOUR WIFE LEFT YOU. YOU DON'T HAVE ENOUGH PASSION. SOMETIMES A WOMAN WANTS TO SEE A MAN BE A MAN. YOU GOTTA PUSH BACK A LITTLE. YOU GOTTA GET A LITTLE ROUGH. OH GOD!!!!!! PETER HIT ME!

I care about the size of your penis as much as you care about the size of my breasts.

★ ★ ★ ★ ★

OH, GOD. I'VE BEEN A WORSE WIFE THAN LORENA BOBBITT WHEN SHE WAS MARRIED TO THE THING.

H-hello? Oh, you must have a wrong number. There's no one here by the name of Long Rod Von Hugen Dong.

You're being silly, Jerome and I dated over twelve inches go.

BRIAN, THIS IS WONDERFUL. I FEEL LIKE ONE OF THE KENNEDYS. YOU KNOW, THE OVER PRIVILEGED DRUNK ONES, NOT THE SOCIALLY RESPONSIBLE DEAD ONES.

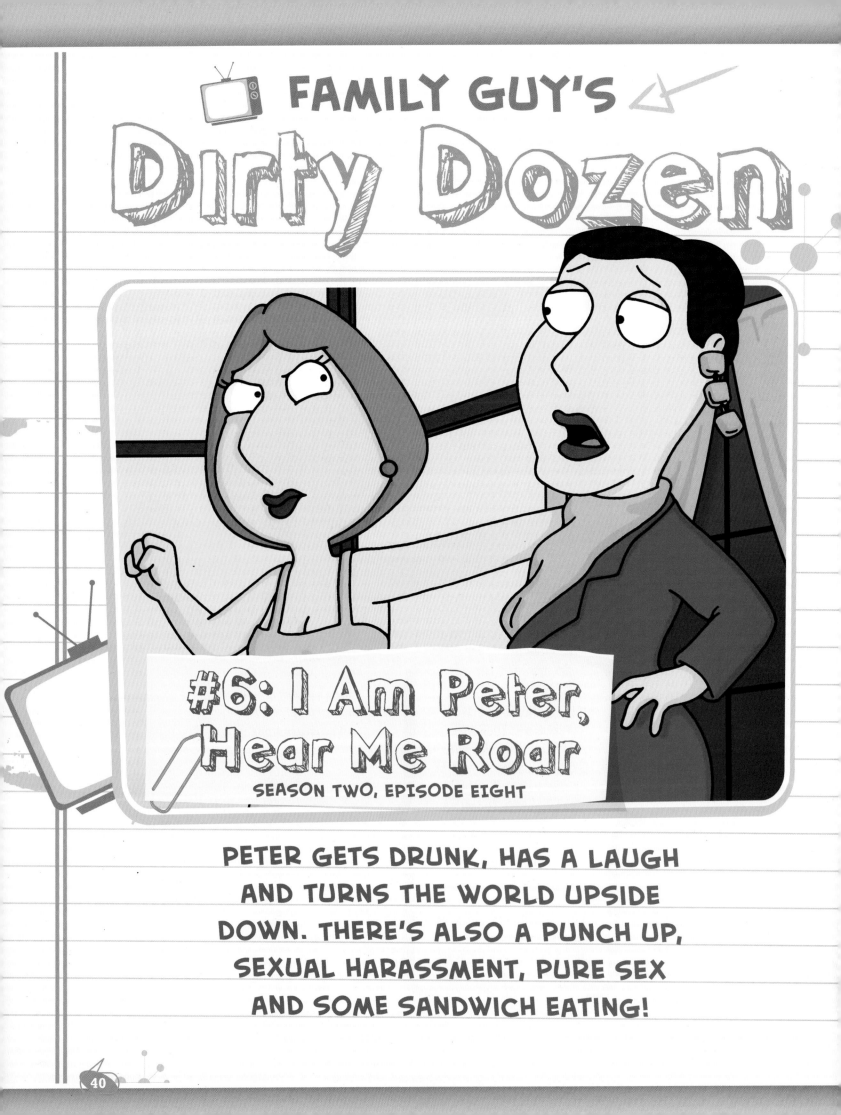

FAMILY GUY'S Dirty Dozen

#6: I Am Peter, Hear Me Roar

SEASON TWO, EPISODE EIGHT

PETER GETS DRUNK, HAS A LAUGH
AND TURNS THE WORLD UPSIDE
DOWN. THERE'S ALSO A PUNCH UP,
SEXUAL HARASSMENT, PURE SEX
AND SOME SANDWICH EATING!

PETER: WHY DO WOMEN HAVE BOOBS? SO YOU GOT SOMETHING TO LOOK AT WHILE YOU'RE TALKING TO THEM.

READ IT!

Peter receives an advert through his letterbox, suggesting he will receive a free boat if he attends a timeshare sales pitch.

During the high-pressure sales situation, Peter trades a boat for a mystery box containing tickets for a comedy club.

At the club, Drunk Peter, Sober Peter's alter-ego, gets on stage to tell jokes. Before being dragged off stage, an upside down beer bottle in his trouser pocket makes it look like he's peed his pants and the crowd laughs.

Drunk Peter thinks the crowd is laughing at his material. Now where is Sober Peter when Drunk Peter needed him?

Thinking he's discovered his funny bone, Sober Peter tells a sexist joke at the Happy-Go-Lucky Toy Factory and offends (whatever that means) co-worker Sarah Bennett.

Benett's lawyer, Gloria Ironbox, offers to drop charges of sexual harassment if Peter goes to a sensitivity training programme, then a women's retreat.

There, he takes his bottom lip and stretches it behind his head to understand a pain comparable to childbirth.

Upon returning home Peter has become extremely sensitive. He spends time in front of the mirror, taking pregnancy tests, scolding Lois for cooking dinner for her husband (him) and breastfeeds Stewie when Lois isn't looking. Lois asks Peter's friends for help.

Cleveland takes Peter to a black convention. Peter publicly tells the men it's their fault for all crime problems. They chase him through the streets believing he's a racist.

Peter and Lois attend a women's gala where Ironbox insults Lois, blaming her for Peter's lack of respect. A punch-up between Gloria and Lois ensues.

Aroused by the scene, Peter gets Lois home to have sex. Lois says how wonderful sex was, which startles Peter – as he had already forgotten that she was in the room.

He asks for a sandwich. Lois knows she has her man back.

KNOW IT!

■ Think Peter is an idiot when, after discovering his feminine side, he tries to give himself a breast exam? Well, it really is possible for men to get breast cancer, so who's the clown now? That's right Coco, you.

■ The title *I am Peter, Hear Me Roar*, is based on a line from the 1972 No.1 song 'I Am Woman' by Helen Reddy.

HEAR IT!

GLORIA IRONBOX: "Mr. Griffin, I'm Gloria Ironbox. I represent one of your co-workers, Sarah Bennett. She's suing you and the company for sexual harassment."

PETER: "Sarah... Sarah... Oh! Is she one we videotaped taking a dump?"

LOIS: "You know, one of these days I'm gonna need the mirror."

PETER: "Oh beans, I can't get this spit curl to... Lois, what day is it?"

LOIS: "Thursday."

PETER: "Oh, my God. Oh. My. God I'm late!"

LOIS: "If you spent less time fixing your hair..."

PETER: "No, Lois, I mean I am 'late' late! Do we still have that pregnancy test?"

LOIS: "Are you insane? You can't have a baby!"

PETER: "Well, I don't have a lot of options, I'm Catholic! God, I thought you'd be happy!"

LOIS: "Anyways Glen, I was wondering if you and Cleveland would help change Peter back to the way he was."

GLEN: "Of course that's why you're here (Glen shuts down his operation to seduce Lois). Don't worry Lois, I'd do everything to you."

LOIS: "What?"

GLEN: "I'd do anything for you."

#6

FAMILY GUY'S Dirty Dozen

#5: Meet the Quagmires
SEASON FIVE, EPISODE 18

TIME TRAVEL CAN LEAD TO ALL SORTS OF PROBLEMS - ESPECIALLY IF YOU CHANGE WHAT HAPPENED IN THE PAST. IMAGINE HOW CONFUSED THINGS COULD BE BACK IN THE PRESENT IF THINGS ARE DIFFERENT. YOU DON'T HAVE TO IMAGINE...

BRIAN: (TO 18-YEAR-OLD LOIS IN 1984) "COULD I WHAM MY OINGO BOINGO INTO YOUR VELVET UNDERGROUND?"

READ IT!

Quagmire brags about his sexual exploits. Peter feels like he's missed out. Death is summoned to The Drunken Clam on a false alarm and grants Peter a wish by sending him and Brian back to 1984 for one night.

Peter is his 18-year-old self. He cancels a date to see the movie Zapped with a pre-marriage Lois, opting instead to hit the bars with Cleveland. Peter enjoys himself, particularly making out with Molly Ringwald. Peter returns to the present.

Back in the present, Peter's future has been changed. He and Molly have been married for 20 years; Lois is married to Quagmire; Al Gore is president; Chris, Meg, and Stewie have Quagmire's chin, nose, and mannerisms. For the love of God!

Peter begs Death a return to the past so he can right the heinous wrongs. Peter is determined to accept Lois' invitation, but repeatedly blows

his chance. Death gets drunk and tells him to fix his own problems – Past Lois is still upset with Past Peter. The ticket to a country club dance she intended to give to Peter goes to Quagmire. In a thinly veiled homage to Back To The Future, Peter and Brian sneak in to the dance to prevent Lois and Quagmire from kissing and falling in love.

They sneak in through the vent but Lois tells Peter he's blown it. As Chris, Stewie, and Meg are disappearing from a family picture, Peter knocks out Quagmire, kisses Lois and wins the girl. Which just goes to show that violence will always win the heart of a woman.

KNOW IT!

■ Meg, Stewie, and Chris are silent throughout the whole episode, apart from the scene where they are Quagmire's children.

■ During the dinner with Quagmire in the alternate present, Lois references Mad TV. Alex Borstein, who voices Lois, was a regular on Mad TV.

■ When Brian is seen on stage at the Country Club Dance singing Rick Astley's hit single 'Never Gonna Give You Up', it is a reference to the Internet

phenomenon known as 'Rick Rolling'. Rick Rolling involves screening the music video as a surprise when surfers are expecting something entertaining.

HEAR IT!

BRIAN: "So, um, have you seen Ghostbusters?"
WOMAN: "Save your breath, geekwad. I'm here with my boyfriend."
BRIAN: "You mean that quintessentially '80s guy, with his collar turned up all the way up?"
MAN WITH A RIDICULOUSLY HIGH COLLAR:
"Are you hitting on my girlfriend?"

QUAGMIRE (TO LOIS):
"Come 'ere baby. Let's go play 'schoolgirl' and 'guy who has sex with schoolgirl'."

WHILE DANCING...
LOIS: "Oh, something poked me!"
QUAGMIRE: "It's ok, it's ok. It's just my wang."

#5

MARVIN: (on the phone) "Hey Rick, it's your cousin Marvin. Marvin Astley. You know that mediocre, generic sound you been lookin' for? Well, listen to this!"

FAMILY GUY'S
Dirty Dozen

#4: Wasted Talent
SEASON TWO, EPISODE TWENTY

BEER THIS! DRINKING BEER CAN MAKE YOU PLAY THE PIANO IN SOME STYLE. WELL, IF YOUR NAME IS PETER IT APPEARS TO WORK. KIDS, DON'T TRY THIS AT HOME, JUST STICK TO THE LESSONS!

PETER: OH LOIS, THANK GOD IT'S YOU! THE LAST THREE HOUSES I WENT TO WERE VERY RUDE.

LOIS: HAVE YOU BEEN DRINKING?

PETER: WHY YES I HAVE... THANK YOU.

READ IT!

Lois is desperate for a piano student who can beat her rival Alexis Radcliffe's student at the piano competition.

At the same time, Peter drinks even more Pawtucket Patriot beer than ever in an attempt to find a Willy Wonka-style hidden silver scroll and win a tour of the brewery.

Joe finds the first silver scroll. Tom Tucker finds the last scroll but later admits he made up the story then puts a meat-eating earwig in his brain to make up for it.

Peter rolls the dice once more and has just one more beer. Before you can say 'a bed full of urine-soaked geriatrics' Peter discovers the final silver scroll and Brian accompanies him to the brewery tour.

Pawtucket Pat is seemingly killed on his front walkway, but the killer turns out to be Cheech Marin hired to pull off a gag.

When it is discovered that the Pawtucket Patriot Brewery doesn't have wheelchair ramps, Joe is forced to leave the tour.

Despite a warning issued by Pawtucket Pat, Peter and Brian splinter off from the group to try the forbidden beer that never goes flat.

When Pat finds Peter and Brian in the forbidden room, he throws them out...

An angry Peter starts bashing at the piano and discovers he can play perfectly when drunk. Lois enters Peter as her student in the piano competition, and keeps him in a state of constant inebriation.

At the repertoire Peter is so drunk that he can't even find the piano but still wins first place with a repertoire of Film and TV theme tunes. In a moment of panic, Lois worries she may have harmed Peter's health for her own selfish needs.

Peter assures her his brain cells are intact. Cut to his final brain cell bending down and breaking his glasses shouting "It's not fair!"

KNOW IT!

■ *Wasted Talent* is the first time Chris had no speaking lines in an episode. There should be more.

■ The end credits show Stewie hitch-hiking along the side of a road in homage to The Hulk's alter ego, David Banner.

HEAR IT!

LOIS: "Peter, it's 7 in the morning."
BRIAN: "Thanks for the update, Big Ben!"
LOIS: "You're drunk again."
PETER: "No, I'm just exhausted because I've been up all night drinking."

CHUMBA WUMBAS: "Chumba Wumba, gobbledy goo. Life isn't fair, it's sad but it's true. Chumba Wumba, gobbledy gee. When your poor legs are stiff as a tree. What do you do when you're stuck in a chair? Finding it hard to go up and down stairs? What do you think of the one you call God? Isn't his absence slightly odd? Maybe he's forgotten you. Chumba Wumba gobbledy gorse. Count yourself lucky, you're not a horse. They would turn you into dog food. Or to Chumba Wumba gobbledy glue."

PETER: "Oh jeez. This hangover's killing me. I haven't felt this crappy since the time I went to that museum. (Flashback to when Peter was a kid) Why did all the dinosaurs die out?"
GUIDE: "Because you touch yourself at night."

#4

Say What?

Peter's had his say about anything and everything. Lois has offered up her own words of wisdom… well, if you can call them that! So now it's the turn of others to shout their mouths off, including Chris, Meg, Cleveland, Mayor West, Tom Tucker and Tricia Takanawa and even a bit of dialogue from Mr Weed…

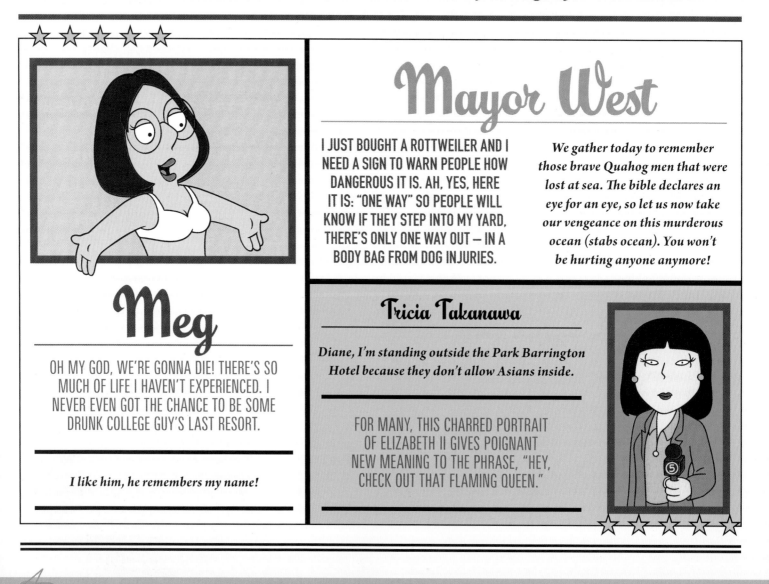

Mayor West

I JUST BOUGHT A ROTTWEILER AND I NEED A SIGN TO WARN PEOPLE HOW DANGEROUS IT IS. AH, YES, HERE IT IS: "ONE WAY" SO PEOPLE WILL KNOW IF THEY STEP INTO MY YARD, THERE'S ONLY ONE WAY OUT — IN A BODY BAG FROM DOG INJURIES.

We gather today to remember those brave Quahog men that were lost at sea. The bible declares an eye for an eye, so let us now take our vengeance on this murderous ocean (stabs ocean). You won't be hurting anyone anymore!

Meg

OH MY GOD, WE'RE GONNA DIE! THERE'S SO MUCH OF LIFE I HAVEN'T EXPERIENCED. I NEVER EVEN GOT THE CHANCE TO BE SOME DRUNK COLLEGE GUY'S LAST RESORT.

I like him, he remembers my name!

Tricia Takanawa

Diane, I'm standing outside the Park Barrington Hotel because they don't allow Asians inside.

FOR MANY, THIS CHARRED PORTRAIT OF ELIZABETH II GIVES POIGNANT NEW MEANING TO THE PHRASE, "HEY, CHECK OUT THAT FLAMING QUEEN."

Cleveland

PUBLIC URINATION IS JUST WRONG. EXCEPT DURING THE MILLION MAN MARCH WHEN PROTESTORS BURNED DOWN OUR PORTA-POTTIES AND I USED MY STREAM OF JUSTICE TO PUT OUT THE HATE.

Oh, Peter, that tickles me in a way, that if Loretta tickled me in that way, I'd say, Oh yea ... that's nice ... that's the spot.

Lois must have written the book on man pleasing. Too bad Loretta doesn't allow white literature in our household.

I CAN'T GET CLEVELAND, JR. TO SIT STILL FOR ANYTHING. SOMETIMES I THINK HE MIGHT HAVE THE EPILEPSY, BUT THEN I JUST GO SEE WHAT'S ON THE TV.

Mr. Weed

PETER, I LIKE YOU. BUT I NEED YOU TO BE MORE THAN JUST EYE CANDY AROUND HERE

Tom Tucker

BECAUSE OF AN ACCIDENT TODAY AT THE QUAHOG CABLE COMPANY, ALL TELEVISION TRANSMISSION WILL BE OUT FOR AN UNDETERMINED AMOUNT OF TIME. OF COURSE, NO ONE CAN SEE THIS NEWS PROGRAMME, SO IT DOESN'T REALLY MATTER WHAT WE SAY. I'M THE LORD JESUS CHRIST. I THINK I'LL GO GET DRUNK AND BEAT UP SOME MIDGETS.

In other news, the man that has done more drugs than any other human being on the planet was killed today by a pack of rabid dogs he thought he saw.

STAY TUNED FOR OUR SPECIAL INVESTIGATIVE REPORT ON THE CLITORIS, NATURE'S RUBIK'S CUBE.

WELL, I BELIEVE I SPEAK FOR EVERYONE WHEN I SAY ALL THE NEW YORKERS CAN GO FORNICATE THEMSELVES WITH A STEEL ROD.

Chris

HEY, DAD, LOOK! I COVERED MY BACK WITH HONEY AND NOW THE ANTS ARE TAKING ME HOME.

I don't have to listen to you! You're a dog! You don't have a soul!

PETER GOES TO ATTACK HUGH GRANT ON THE MOVIE SCREEN: DON'T DO IT, DAD! HE'S BIGGER THAN YOU!

When I stick this army guy with the sharp bayonette up my nose, it tickles my brain. Hah hah hah ... ow. Oh, now I don't know math.

MY NAME IS CHRIS, I'M SUPPOSED TO BE ON MY BEST BEHAVIOUR TONIGHT AND NOT MENTION POO..... OH GOD, WHAT HAVE I DONE?

I'm so hungry I could ride a horse. I don't get it. Well, I could ride it to the store, I guess.

I NEVER KNEW ANYONE WHO WENT CRAZY BEFORE, EXCEPT FOR MY INVISIBLE FRIEND, COL. SCHWARTZ.

IT'S PARTIALLY AN EXPRESSION OF MY TEENAGE ANGST... BUT MOSTLY, IT'S A MOO COW!

FAMILY GUY'S
Dirty Dozen

#3: Let's Go To The Hop
SEASON TWO, EPISODE FOURTEEN

A TOAD-LICKING PROBLEM ARISES AT JAMES WOODS HIGH, AND LOIS AND PETER BECOME CONCERNED.

**PETER GRIFFIN ON HIS FIRST LOVE, PHOEBE DIAMOND:
I HAD SUCH A CRUSH ON HER... UNTIL I MET
YOU, LOIS. YOU'RE MY SILVER MEDAL.**

READ IT!

Lois and Peter find a toad in Chris' pocket and they suspect him as being a toad licker. However, they discover that the toad was Meg's property and she was holding the toad for one of the popular kids in the vain hope that doing so would get her a date to the Winter Snow Ball.

Lois and Peter decide they need to do something to protect their kids from this toad-licking drug problem.

Peter talks to Meg's principal and arranges to go undercover at the school as Lando Griffin.

Despite Meg's fears, that the appearance of Lando Griffin will make her ever less popular, when Peter smashes his hand on a cafeteria juke-box, he becomes the man about campus.

Lando convinces the kids it's not cool to lick toad. Meg, seeing an opportunity, tells the cool kids

that Lando has asked her to the Winter Snow Ball, which immediately increases her popularity.

Peter is enjoying his High School experience a little too much, taking great delight in farting loudly in class to make the guys laugh and girls vomit.

Despite agreeing to go to the ball with Meg, he stands her up and goes with Meg's nemesis Connie D'Amico.

Meg goes to the dance by herself and Lando (Peter) tells the crowd that Meg was really his first choice as a date.

Meg gets lots of attention as Lando drives recklessly off into the night.

The next day, although no body is found, the news reports that Lando died when he went off Deadman's Curve. Police decided it was best to get on with life.

KNOW IT!

■ While some toads do produce venom that can cause a hallucination, licking toads is unlikely to cause such a strong effect. There is no actual species of toad called the Colombian Spotted Toad, it was deliberately made up.

■ At the beginning of the episode the two Colombians speak nonsensical Spanish with Korean subtitles. The first Columbian says: "If the boss finds out, we're dead." The second asks: "Did you remember to close the garage door this morning?"

■ In this episode, Chris mentions Meg strangling their other sister to prove she could do bad things. This is something Lois and Peter quickly and suspiciously dismiss.

HEAR IT!

PETER: "Gregg Allman, how did you handle it when life got you down?"

GREGG ALLMAN: (emerging from a poster) "Me? I did a lot of drugs, married some broad named Cher. I wouldn't recommend either one of 'em."

PETER: "You'll get chills all through your body
And you'll lose all control
Of your bladder and your sphincter
That's your butt hole
Cause if you use toad
Then I'm telling you
You can kiss your life goodbye
Yeah, when you use toad
It'll mess you up
It'll make your mama cry, that's no lie
You'll choke on your tongue and die
Gotta give it up."

#3

FAMILY GUY'S
Dirty Dozen

#2: PTV
SEASON FOUR, EPISODE FOURTEEN

CENSOR TV? OK, NO PROBLEM, JUST LEAVE OUR FAMILY
GUY AND THE CLEVELAND SHOW ALONE! PETER RUNS INTO
A LOT OF PROGRAMME PROBLEMS WHEN HE SETS UP HIS
OWN TV CHANNEL – INCLUDING HAVING HIS LIFE CENSORED!

STEWIE: GOOD DAY TO YOU SIR. AND NOW PREPARE TO DIE.

#2

READ IT!

During the Emmys Niles Crane's, aka David Hyde Pierce, trousers malfunction and his testicles appear which prompts the Federal Communications Commission (FCC) to censor television.

Peter is having none of it and decides to set up his own TV Channel called PTV.

Peter screens uncut, unedited and uncompromising programming, such as Midnight Q which features Quagmire sat naked in his bachelor pad: "Welcome to Midnight Q. Tonight, we're going to enjoy the smooth jazz of Charles Mingus, Norman Mailer is here to read an excerpt from his latest book, and then we also have a girl from Omaha who's hiding a banana. We'll find out where. Giggity-giggity, giggity-goo. Stick around." There's also Dogs Humping and The Peter Griffin Side-Boob Hour, which becomes an amazing success. Brian and Stewie have their own show, Cheeky Bastard.

Lois, outraged by Peter's programming, calls in the FCC to shut PTV down. Peter claims that the FCC can't stop people from being who they are so, to prove a point,

the FCC starts censoring lives.

They put a black censor's bar over Peter's parts, swearing is overdubbed with airhorns and farts banned in public.

Even sex is banned: "Oh, you can have sex, just no moaning, no tongue-kissing, no thrusting, no movement whatsoever" which makes raunchy Lois feel frustrated and guilty.

Peter makes the FCC back off after he notes how many famous American buildings resemble body parts.

Peter ends the FCC oppression and the Griffins settle down to watch an episode of the The Brady Bunch. Which includes a poo joke.

KNOW IT!

■ The PTV opening includes references to The Naked Gun films, The Wizard of Oz, The Shining, Ben-Hur, Doom, and The Sound of Music.

■ In the episode, The FCC censor two-fifths of the title from The Dick Van Dyke Show.

HEAR IT!

THE FELLAS AT THE FREAKIN' FCC SONG WITH PETER, STEWIE & BRIAN

"They will clean up all your talking
in a matter such as this
They will make you take a tinkle
when you want to take a p*ss
And they'll make you call fellatio
a trouser-friendly kiss
Here's the plain situation!
There's no negotiation!
With the fellows at the freakin FCC!
They're as stuffy as the stuffiest of
the special interest groups...
Make a joke about your bowels
and they order in the troops
Any baby with a brain could tell
them everybody poops!
Take a tip, take a lesson! You'll
never win by messin'
With the fellas at the freakin' FCC
And if you find yourself with
some young sexy thing
You're gonna have to do her
with your ding-a-ling
Cause you can't say penis!
So they sent this little warning
they're prepared to do the worst
And they stuck it in your
mailbox hoping you
could be co-erced
I can think of quite
another place they should
have stuck it first!
They may just be neurotic
Or possible psychotic
They're the fellas at
the freakin FCC!"

FAMILY GUY'S Dirty Dozen

#1: Road to the Multiverse
SERIES EIGHT, EPISODE ONE

PIG MUTATIONS, REMOTE CONTROLLERS THAT TRANSPORT BETWEEN ALTERNATE UNIVERSES AND PLANETS WHERE DOGS RULE. BUT WHO BIT WHO? WAS IT HUMAN WHO BIT DOG, OR CANINE THAT CHEWED ITS MASTER?

READ IT!

Brian and Stewie are at The Quahog Clam Day Fair and Stewie wins an animal contest using a pig with incredible muscles and fists, think of a cross between Martina Navratilova and a pig.

Brian is curious about how Stewie got hold of such pig and Stewie explains he got it from a farm that breeds specially mutated animals. Brian insists on seeing the farm so Stewie lets him in on his Multiverse Theory and shows him a remote control that can transport them around alternate universes.

They travel to the universe where Stewie got the pig, a scientifically advanced one where Christianity never existed. They visit a universe of half-naked men - Stewie: Love it! Brian: Hate it. In the two headed universe, Happy Stewie is French-kissing Sad Stewie.

Eventually, they stumble upon a universe where dogs rule humans. Brian loves it, gets into a scuffle with Stewie over the remote and breaks it, trapping them in this universe.

In desperation, the two go to the dogs-rule-humans version of the Griffin family. The Griffins are all dogs, but Brian is a human. In the Dog World, Lois is a cocker spaniel, Chris a sheepdog, Meg a bulldog, Stewie a poodle, Joe a Doberman and Tom Tucker a brown and yellow mongrel. Peter looks like a brown bear.

THE QUAHOG CLAM DAY FAIR, MAYOR WEST IS AT A 'GUESS YOUR WEIGHT' BOOTH

CARNY: LET'S SEE. I GUESS 185 LBS. (WEST STEPS ON THE SCALE AND COMES OUT 0.15LBS)

WEST: WRONG. I'M 95% HELIUM. (HE FLOATS AWAY WHILE TAKING HIS PRIZE)

Dog Stewie reveals he also has a multiverse device (which will allow Dog Brian and Human Stewie to return to reality).

Before they can use it Human Stewie bites Dog Peter. Human Stewie is about to be put to sleep but escapes, with Dog Brian, from the Human Pound in the nick of time.

Human Brian also jumps through the portal to begin a new exciting life in a new exciting universe where humans are on top… and is immediately killed by a car.

up the Cuban Missile Crisis and plunged the Earth into World War III

- Universe blocky, low resolution
- Universe fire hydrants
- Universe homosexuals
- Universe Real
- Universe faraway guy yells compliments
- Universe misleading portraits
- Universe human/ dog role reversal
- Universe Family Guy

KNOW IT!

- A few of the universes visited…
  - *Universe where Christianity never existed*
  - *Universe where WWII Japan invaded USA*
  - *Universe Two Heads, One happy, one sad.*
  - *Universe Ice Age*
  - *Universe where everyone needs a pooh*
  - *Universe where Nixon won, botched*

HEAR IT!

STEWIE: "What time do you suppose it is, Brian?"

BRIAN: "I don't know, about 3:30?"

STEWIE: "Watch the sidewalk." (Brian looks over to the other side of the street to see a sexy version of Meg walking down the road while Van Halen's *Drop Dead Legs* plays)

BRIAN: "My god, is that… Meg?"

STEWIE: "36D Brian. And you know what's amazing? In this universe she's still one of the ugly ones. If you saw Lois, you'd have to put your penis in a wheelchair."

(IN JAPANESE UNIVERSE)

STEWIE: "According to the multiverse guide, this is a universe where the United States never dropped the atomic bomb on Hiroshima. So the Japanese just never quit." (Speaking in Japanese)

JAPANESE PETER: "Meg, you ugly and dishonourable."

JAPANESE MEG: "I make obedience to father wish." (Meg commits suicide)

JAPANESE PETER: "I fart now." (He stands up and farts on Meg's corpse)

JAPANESE CHRIS: "Now I laugh because he fart. Ha ha ha ha! Now I done with laugh."

JAPANESE QUAGMIRE: (entering the Griffin's house) "Hello, I like many sex. Goodbye."

JAPANESE STEWIE: "I no like you, but I like you!"

JAPANESE BRIAN: "I no like you, but I like you, too!"

JAPANESE LOIS: (coming in with sushi for Peter) "I honour your penis by bringing it food."

JAPANESE PETER: "My penis hungry two hour ago!" (Punches Lois and she leaves giggling)

SO, YOU THINK YOU KNOW...
PETER GRIFFIN?

QUESTION 1
On whom did Seth MacFarlane base the voice of Peter Griffin?

QUESTION 2
What is the name of Peter's real father?

QUESTION 3
What is the name of Peter's arch nemesis The Giant Chicken?

QUESTION 4
In which country was Peter born?

QUESTION 5
Which fast food joint used Peter as their TV ambassador in 2008?

SO, YOU THINK YOU KNOW...

THE PATRIARCH OF THE GRIFFIN FAMILY HAS NO IDEA WHAT THE WORD PATRIARCH MEANS. WHILE PETER LIKES THE OCCASIONAL ADULT BEVERAGE AT THE DRUNKEN CLAM, HIS REAL PASSIONS ARE HAIR-BRAINED SCHEMES AND PUBLIC NUDITY. HE IS A MAN WHO KNOWS WHAT HE LIKES AND LIKES WHAT LITTLE HE KNOWS. BUT HOW MUCH DO YOU KNOW ABOUT PETER GRIFFIN? AND, MORE PERTINENTLY, ACTUALLY CARE?

QUESTION 6
What was Peter doing when he first met Lois?

QUESTION 7
Which instrument did Peter play at Junior College?

QUESTION 8
Which instrument can Peter play perfectly when perfectly drunk?

QUESTION 9
In which episode did Peter undergo a vasectomy?

QUESTION 10
In *Fifteen Minutes of Shame*, how does Peter announce that he's finished having sex with Lois?

QUESTION 11
In *Peter And Bill's Bogus Journey*, who does Peter catch Lois in bed with?

QUESTION 12
What is Peter's favourite song?

QUESTION 13
Peter is having his picture taken for his driving licence. What does he do so that if he is pulled over he won't get caught?

QUESTION 14
In *Perfect Castaway*, who did Peter out-fart in a duelling fart-off?

QUESTION 15
What was the name of the television channel set up by Peter?

QUESTION 16
What was the name of the country started by Peter?

QUESTION 17
What is the name of Peter's male boss?

QUESTION 18
What is the name of the restaurant Peter opens that refuses to allow disabled people?

QUESTION 19
When Peter made his own religion, who did he worship?

QUESTION 20
Which famous American Football team did Peter play for?

Singalonga **STEWIE**

IT IS CRUEL, YOU KNOW, THAT MUSIC SHOULD BE SO BEAUTIFUL. IT HAS THE BEAUTY OF LONELINESS OF PAIN: OF STRENGTH AND FREEDOM. THE BEAUTY OF DISAPPOINTMENT AND NEVER-SATISFIED LOVE. THE CRUEL BEAUTY OF NATURE AND EVERLASTING BEAUTY OF MONOTONY.

LIVE PERFORMANCE

STEWIE GRIFFIN SOMETIMES JUST GETS THE URGE TO DANCE! HE'S ALSO THEN GOTTA SING ALONG TO THE TUNES BECAUSE MUSIC IS IN HIS BLOOD. HE CLAIMS TO COME FROM A VERY MUSICAL FAMILY — A DYSFUNCTIONAL FAMILY, BUT A MUSICAL FAMILY. IN FACT, WE THINK STEWIE MIGHT HAVE A SECRET AMBITION TO BE A MAJOR ROCK STAR OR A CLASSY CROONER. HE'S OFTEN PUMPED FULL OF WIDE-EYED EXCITEMENT AND WONDER.

Stewie particularly enjoys Family Guy's musical numbers and we have listed here seven of the ditties he has enjoyed the most. It was a tough decision. The vote could have gone anyway but we decided on the songs Stewie brought to life: You Can Find It On TV… *ABC has got a line-up that's refreshing and alive. With its hits like Desperate Housewives just continuing to thrive. And those women look sensational for being sixty-five…* or My Fat Baby *Oh my fat baby loves to eat. A big ol' Buddha belly and her breast swing past her feet. My fat baby loves to eat. My big ol' fatass baby loves to eat.* Stewie reckons he has to give credit to the fat man – who he says can carry a tune just about as well as Nicaraguan bell boy looking for a tip carries heavy luggage. Peter can sing, he can dance and he can act. But first let's hear it for Stewie as he guides us through his favourite seven Family Guy show tunes. Life is indeed a cabaret, old chum.

★ SOMEWHERE THAT'S GREEN ★

Stewie has often wondered what Herbert sees in Chris. Stewie believes he is more rugged, more intelligent and, in many ways, more manly than Chris! This song, part of the musical score for the film adaptation of *Little Shop of Horrors*, was performed by Herbert in The Courtship of Stewie's Father. Herbert sings the song to Chris after the fat boy is ordered to do chores for breaking Herbert's window. The sequence was originally sung by a woman, Audrey, declaring her love for Rick Moranis' Seymour (the geeky looking guy in Ghostbusters who almost gets it on with Sigourney Weaver). Stewie can never can make his mind up about Sigourney Weaver. Is she a woman who looks a little bit like a man, or a man who looks a little like a woman? Or an alienmanwoman? Anyhoo, we digress, there is a good chance she's not of this world, y' know?). Here's the song. Singalong?

HERBERT:

He rakes and trims the grass,
He loves to mow and weed,
I cook like Betty Crocker,
And I look like Donna Reed.
There's plastic on my furniture
To keep it neat and clean,
In the Pine-Sol scented air,
Somewhere that's green.
Between our frozen dinners
And our bedtime, 9:15,
We snuggle watching Lucy,
On our big, enormous 12-inch screen.
I'm his December bride,
Chris Griffin, he knows best.
The kids play Howdy-Doody,
As the sun sets in the west.
A picture out of "Better Homes
and Gardens Magazine,"
Someday I know,
We two will go,
Somewhere that's green.

Singalonga STEWIE

▶ PLAY

The song *I need a Jew* came from the episode *When You Wish Upon A Weinstein*. This was an episode that caused more outrage than a Celine Dion concert, despite the fact that the episode's writer, Ricky Blitt, is as Jewish as a diamond collector's nose. Enjoy.

★ I NEED A JEW ★

PETER:
Nothing else has worked so far,
So I'll wish upon a star,
Wondrous dancing speck of light,
I need a Jew...

Lois makes me take the rap,
Cause our checkbook looks like crap,
Since I can't give her a slap,
I need a Jew...

Where to find
A Baum or Stien or Stein
To teach me how to whine
And do my taxes...

Though by many they're abhorred,
Hebrew people I've adored,
Even though they killed my Lord,
I need a Jew! (A kock at the door...)

MAX:
Hi, my name's Max Weinstein. My car just
broke down, may I use your phone?

PETER:
Now my troubles are all through I have a Jew!

MAX:
Hey!

★ PROM NIGHT ★ DUMPSTER BABY

This song, from *Airport '07*, has absolutely nothing to do with Melissa Drexler. Stewie believes he should have been the lead in this song – but the producers said he was outside the age cohort. Hey, come on, he's one-year-old and already being typecast! Here's a question for you, continuity guys... these are newborn babies right? New born and they can walk, dance and sing? Stewie can also walk, dance and sing and play the part. Give him a chance!

BABY :	I'm just a prom night dumpster baby I got no mom, or dad Prom night dumpster baby My story isn't long but boy it's awfully sad
BACKUP BABY SINGERS	Ba-ba-ba-ba-bum
BABY	And though I came from a hole
BACKUP BABY SINGERS	And though he came from a hole
BABY	I'm singin' right from the soul
BACKUP BABY SINGERS	He's singin' right from the soul
BABY	My fanny needs a blanket And somebody to spank it I miss my mom
BASS BABY	But she's at the prom
ALL BABIES	So I'm a prom night dumpster baby. Prom night dumpster baby Ba-ba-ba-ba-ba-ba-ba-bum
BABY	And I'm takin' a stroll
BACKUP BABY SINGERS	He's takin' a stroll
BABY	I'm takin' a stroll
BACKUP BABY SINGERS	He's takin' a stroll
BABY	I'm takin' a stroll
BACKUP BABY SINGERS	He's takin' a stroll
BABY	Uh huh-huh-huh-huh – I'm takin' a stroll
BACKUP BABY SINGERS	He's takin' a stroll
BABY	I'm takin' a stroll

PLAY

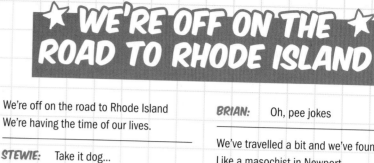

★ WE'RE OFF ON THE ★ ROAD TO RHODE ISLAND

A duet between Brian and Stewie from the episode of the same name, *We're off on the road to Rhode Island* is the pair's parody of the "Road to..." songs.

We're off on the road to Rhode Island
We're having the time of our lives.

STEWIE: Take it dog...

BRIAN: We're quite a pair of partners,
Just Like Thelma and Louise.
'cept you're not six feet tall

STEWIE: Yes and your breasts
don't reach your knees.

BRIAN: Give it time.

We're off on the road to Rhode Island,
We're certainly going in style.

BRIAN: I'm with an intellectual, who
craps inside his pants.

STEWIE: How dare you. At least I don't
leave urine stains on all the
household plants.

BRIAN: Oh, pee jokes

We've travelled a bit and we've found,
Like a masochist in Newport
we're Rhode Island bound.

BRIAN: Crazy travel conditions, huh?

STEWIE: First class or no class

BRIAN: Whoa, careful with that
joke, it's an antique

We're off on the road to Rhode Island
We're not going to stop until we're there

BRIAN: Maybe for a beer.

BRIAN: Whatever dangers we may
face, we'll never fear or cry

STEWIE: That's right, until we're
syndicated Fox will never
let us die (Please!)

We're off on the road to Rhode Island,
The home of that old campus swing.

BRIAN: We may pick up some college
girls, and picnic on the grass.

STEWIE: We'd tell you more, but
we'd have the censors
on our ass. (Yikes!)

We're off on the road to Rhode Island
We certainly do get around.

Like a bunch of renegade pilgrims
who are thrown out of Plymouth
colony. We're Rhode Island bound.
Or like a group of College Freshmen
who were rejected by Harvard
and forced to go to Brown. We're
RHODE ISLAND BOUND

Welcome to a moment of reverie, bonhomie and jolly good singalong fun. In this political tome from the episode *PTV*, Stewie was joined by the fat man and Brian for a sideways swipe against censorial America. As Brian might say, this is really one in the eye for the man... And Stewie knows all about giving the man one in the eye, such are the joy of infant incontinence. You may not know this, trivia fans, but the tune for The FCC song is taken from Volunteer Fire Picnic, a song from an almost anonymous 1959 Broadway Musical Take Me Along which starred Jackie Gleason. Javeh! Why not singalong with Stewie right now? Go on, get it on YouTube, you know you want to.

★ THE FREAKIN' FCC ★

PETER: Oh yeah, I know all about the FCC! They will clean up all your talking in a manner such as this

BRIAN: They will make you take a tinkle when you want to take a piss

STEWIE: And they'll make you call fellatio a trouser-friendly kiss

PETER, BRIAN & STEWIE: It's the plain situation! There's no negotiation!

PETER: With the fellas at the freakin FCC!

BRIAN: They're as stuffy as the stuffiest of special interest groups...

PETER: Make a joke about your bowels and they order in the troops

STEWIE: Any baby with a brain could tell them everybody poops!

PETER, BRIAN & STEWIE: Take a tip, take a lesson! You'll never win by messin

PETER: With the fellas at the freakin' FCC
And if you find yourself with some young sexy thing
You're gonna have to do her with your ding-a-ling,
Cause you can't say penis!
So they sent this little warning they're prepared to do their worst

BRIAN: And they stuck it in your mailbox hoping you could be coerced

STEWIE: I can think of quite another place they should have stuck it first!

PETER, BRIAN & STEWIE: They may just be neurotic or possibly psychotic
They're the fellas at the freakin FCC!

THIS HOUSE IS ★ FREAKIN' SWEET ★

This House is Freakin' Sweet is performed in *Peter, Peter, Caviar Eater* by the fat man and employees of Cherrywood Manor, with voices from many others. The number is a reference to the song *I Think I'm Going to Like It Here* from the wonderful musical, *Annie*. The song was nominated for an Emmy for Outstanding Music and Lyrics but lost out to Up to You from Nickelodeon millennium special Nickellennium.

SERVANTS:	We only live to kiss your ass.
SEBASTIAN:	Kiss it? Hell, we'll even wipe it for you!
SERVANTS:	From here on in, it's Easy Street.
PETER:	Any bars on that street?
SEBASTIAN:	24 happy hours a day.
PETER:	Oh, boy!
SERVANTS:	We'll stop Jehovah's at the gate.
GUARD:	Can I see that pamphlet, sir? (Whacks Jehovah's Witness with the pamphlet and smiles?)
PETER:	My God, this house is freakin' sweet.
CHEF:	I make brunch, Clive cooks lunch, each and every day.
BLAKE:	Chocolate cake, a la Blake!
PETER:	Hundred bucks, Blake is gay.
SERVANTS:	We'll do the best we can with Meg.
MEG:	Are you sayin' I'm ugly?
SERVANT:	It doesn't matter, dear. You're rich now!
SERVANTS:	We'll do your nails and rub your feet.

LOIS:	Oh that's not necess-oh my.
SERVANTS:	We'll do your homework every night.
CHRIS:	It's really hard.
SEBASTIAN:	That's why we got that Stephen Hawking guy.
PETER:	My God, this house is freakin' sweet! Used to pass lots of gas; Lois ran away. Now we've got 30 rooms! Hello, beans. Goodbye, spray!
SERVANTS:	We'd take a bullet just for you.
STEWIE:	Oh, what a coincidence, I've got one.
LOIS:	Stewie!
SERVANTS:	Prepare to suck that golden teet. Now that you're stinking rich, we'll gladly be your bitch.
PETER:	My god, this house is-
ALL:	freakin' sweet! Welcome!
SERVANT (TALKING):	That's a wrap, people. Now let's get the hell out of here.
PETER:	Wait a second, where you going?
SERVANT:	The old bag only paid us up through the song.

LOIS:	Well, we can just pick up after ourselves. After all, we'll only be here on weekends.
PETER:	No no, Lois. It's time you started living like the piece of Schmidt you are.
LOIS:	That's 'Pewterschmidt.'
PETER:	W-W-Wait, you guys! You guys, you're all hired to be full time Griffin servants.
LOIS:	Peter, where are we going to get the money to pay all these people?
PETER:	Simple. I, eh, sold our house in Quahog.
LOIS:	You sold our home?!
PETER:	Surprise!
LOIS:	Peter, how could you?
PETER:	Whoops. *Singing.* I recognise that tone. Tonight I sleep alone.
ALL:	But still this house is freakin' sweet!

Singalonga STEWIE

In *Sibling Rivalry*, when Bertram and Stewie go head-to-head, Peter decides to have a vasectomy. Stewie often wonders what might have been had the fat man not been the one to fertilise the fresh eggs of Mummy. Imagine, a Meg with charisma and charm, a Chris with a waistline and then Stewie... just think what he could have been had it not been for the genetic inertia inflicted upon him by the semen of a man who tries to eat staplers. By the way, there's a goof in this song – notice the bass singer? He is blonde at the beginning of the number but for a close up he has ginger hair. The next shot he pokes his head under the chair and he is blonde again! Jeesh, you'd have thought the simple process of colouring in would be the most basic pre-requisite for a cartoon show, would you not?
Now Sing!

★ VASECTOMY ★

QUARTET: A vasectomy's a medical procedure
One that makes you half a man. You're half a man
Remember when you twisted up your garden hose
Well, essentially, that is the plan (That is the plan)

PETER: Well, I'm startin' to get the picture, but how's it done

QUARTET: You make a small incision in the scrotal skin, isolate the vas and then, isolate the vas and then, you hold it in position with a towel clamp, then you snip the fibrous tissue

BASS SOLO: Then you snip the fibrous tissue

QUARTET: Hey but you'll never have to wear a condom when you do it with your wife ...or anyone else you do it with. We promise not to tell, like that new hot chick at work. You know, the one who always has high beams under her ribbed-white cotton T-shirt, but then stares daggers at you for checking her out, and it's like, why do you wear that if you don't want attention? But you know you shouldn't think that way because of the sexual harassment meeting you all had to go to. Seriously, how lame was that? And you couldn't help but notice that the female lawyer running the seminar had a huge rack, like, ridiculously huge for someone who has to talk about that kind of stuff. Well, I guess that's the definition of the word... I-ron-y

GOODBYE SAY GOODBYE TO MANHOOD
GOODBYE SAY GOODBYE TO BABIES
GOODBYE SAY GOODBYE
TO KIDS LIKE MEG

BASS SOLO: Vacuum out your sack

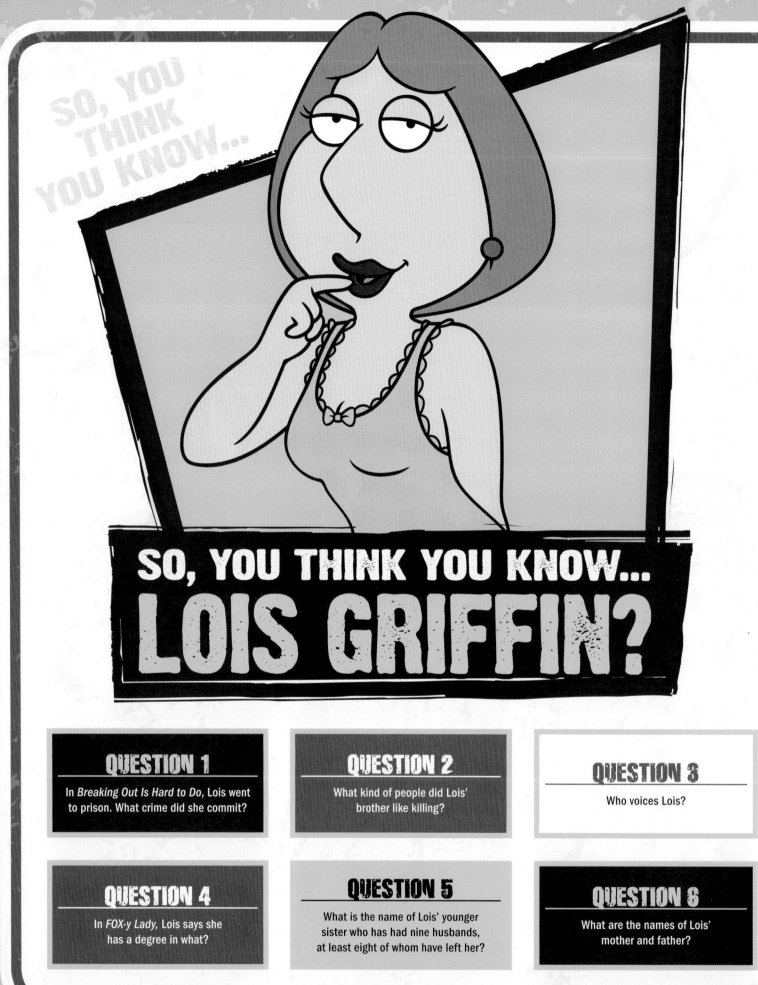

SO, YOU THINK YOU KNOW... LOIS GRIFFIN?

QUESTION 1

In *Breaking Out Is Hard to Do*, Lois went to prison. What crime did she commit?

QUESTION 2

What kind of people did Lois' brother like killing?

QUESTION 3

Who voices Lois?

QUESTION 4

In *FOX-y Lady*, Lois says she has a degree in what?

QUESTION 5

What is the name of Lois' younger sister who has had nine husbands, at least eight of whom have left her?

QUESTION 6

What are the names of Lois' mother and father?

YOU THINK YOU KNOW LOIS? YOU THINK YOU KNOW WHAT IT'S LIKE TO SPEND YOUR LIFE WIPING STEWIE'S BUTT? AND PETER'S? TO HAVE A SON WHO IS PART-BOY, PART-ELEPHANT AND A DAUGHTER WITH THE SEXUAL CHARM OF A TOILET BRUSH? YOU THINK YOU KNOW LOIS? LET'S SEE WHAT YOU REALLY KNOW ABOUT THE GRIFFIN'S HIGH-PITCHED VOICE OF REASON.

QUESTION 7
In the original pitch of *Family Guy* to Fox, what was different about Lois' appearance?

QUESTION 8
In *Family Goy*, what does Lois discover about her Mom?

QUESTION 9
As a teen Lois was crowned as which State's beauty queen?

QUESTION 10
When Lois was with the rock band KISS, what was her nickname?

QUESTION 11
Tough one: in which three episodes did Lois date Quagmire?

QUESTION 12
At the time she fell pregnant with Meg, Lois was selected for the Olympics to compete in which sport?

QUESTION 13
In the episode *Perfect Castaway*, who did Lois marry, thinking that Peter was dead?

QUESTION 14
Lois used to be a circus freak, a dwarf-like creature, who used a trampoline and shouted what?

QUESTION 15
In Petarded, it is revealed that Lois has acquired which medical condition caused by repressing the fact that her husband is an arrogant moron? Which condition?

QUESTION 16
Revealed in *Lethal Weapons*, Lois has which colour Tae-Jitsu belt?

QUESTION 17
When, in *Barely Legal*, Peter accidentally shoots Lois, what does she ask him to do to the bullet hole?

QUESTION 18
Which European country are Lois' parents from?

QUESTION 19
What does Peter's staunch Roman Catholic father, Francis, spray paint underneath the 'Just Married' sign on the back of her and Peter's wedding car?

QUESTION 20
Which musical instrument does Lois teach?

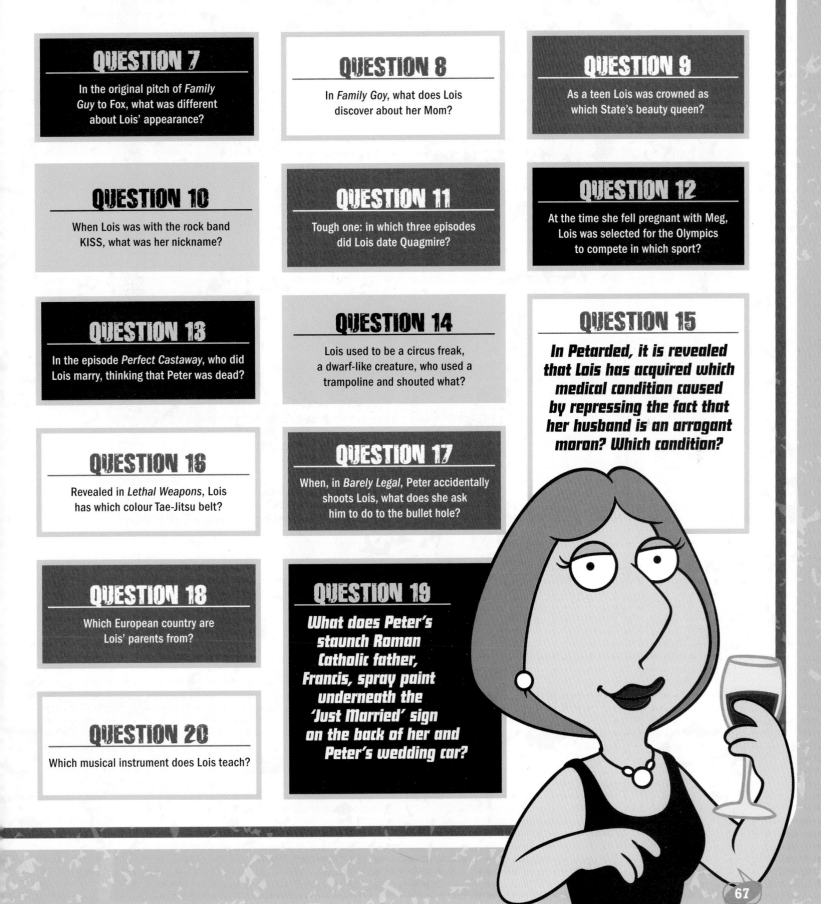

QUAHOG TV

Quahog 5 News, aka Channel Five Action News, is the local news station to Quahog. It is also broadcast live and direct to Providence and Boston. The show is helmed by Tom Tucker. Tucker is an anchorman who is narcissistic, arrogant and dismissive and once broke off a news broadcast to claim: "Oh, hang on a second, there's a handsome man in this spoon."

Tom's racist co-anchor is Diane Simmons. His other colleagues are Asian reporter Tricia Takanawa. Takanawa has an unhealthy obsession with David Bowie, as she displayed when she met him in *Stewie Griffin: The Untold Story*: "Oh! Make love to me Ziggy Stardust! I take you home! I make you fish ball soup! Fish ball!"

There's also Hispanic reporter Maria Jimen... Jim... Jimena... and weatherman Ollie Williams. Ollie was once replaced by Greg the Weather Mime.

In The News...

They've had a lot of good times at WQHG. Like the time Lando Griffin, a popular student at a local high school, was killed when his motorcycle careered off dead man's curve. Police were baffled when no body was found at the scene, but decided it was best not to ask questions and just let everyone get on with their lives.

Or there was the time that the man who has done more drugs than any other human on the planet was killed by a pack of rabid dogs he thought he saw.

There was also the investigative report on the clitoris: Nature's Rubik's Cube, and the piece on a loveable little pig that Jews refuse to eat.

Diane once reported from Quahog's Special Games where she watched some of Quahog's bravest athletes struggle valiantly against God's twisted designs. Viewers cheered, viewers cried, they even got a cheap laugh or two.

Tom, who enjoys a dash of urine in his coffee, also reported on a sexy new trend that emerged at James Woods High. It appeared that students had taken to having ear sex in lieu of traditional intercourse. Over 200 reports of ear sex were confirmed prompting a new slogan: Once you go black, you go deaf.

Among Tom's many low lights, in *Wasted Talent*, he admitted live on air that he'd lied about the last Pawtucket scroll being found. "That's right! I made it up. I figured if people thought the last scroll was found, everyone would stop looking, giving me the edge to find it myself. What I did was wrong... and as an act of contrition, I will now insert this carnivorous earwig into my brain. Heh... kinda tickles.

Ahh!!! Ahh!!! Oh God!!! It's eating out the back of my eyes!!! Ahh!!!"

Diane Simmons plain just don't like black people. She is, however, a dedicated actress having played bit parts in art films at University. She was all set to play Anna in 'The King and I' before Peter changed the script so massively, that Anna turned from a British school teacher into a male cybernetic assassin from the future.

Tom: "Because of an accident today at the Quahog cable company, all television transmissions will be out for an undetermined amount of time. Of course, no one can see this news programme, so it doesn't really matter what we say. I'm the Lord Jesus Christ. I think I'll go get drunk and beat up some midgets, how about you, Diane?"

Diane: "Tom, you're so deep in the closet, you're finding Christmas presents."

Tricia: "Watch as I have sex with this dangerous man."

Ollie: "It's gonna rain!"

SO, YOU THINK YOU KNOW... CHRIS GRIFFIN?

QUESTION 1
What was the name Chris used when he was an artist?

QUESTION 2
How old is Chris?

QUESTION 3
What is the name of the school that Chris attends?

QUESTION 4
Chris wouldn't hurt a fly unless it landed on a... what?

QUESTION 5
Who used to live in Chris's closet and now lives with Jake Turner?

LIKE ANY TYPICAL TEEN, CHRIS HAS A FONDNESS FOR, UM, SELF DISCOVERY. HE MIGHT BE A TALENTED ARTIST AND HAVE AN INCREDIBLE KNOWLEDGE OF VIDEO GAMES, MOVIES AND SOFT PORN, BUT WHEN IT COMES TO JUST ABOUT EVERYTHING ELSE, HE'S NOT THE SHARPEST PENCIL IN THE BOX. HELL, HE'S NOT EVEN THE SHARPEST ERASER. SOME DAY CHRIS HOPES TO BE AS DUMB AS HIS FATHER.

QUESTION 6
In *When You Wish Upon a Weinstein*, what religion does Chris convert to because Peter tells him they are smarter and more successful?

QUESTION 7
Revealed in Season Three, what is Chris' favourite ice cream flavour?

QUESTION 8
In *E. Peterbus Unum*, while being home schooled by Lois, Chris passes Meg a note. What is written on it?

QUESTION 9
Chris is the object of the affections of a local elderly paedophile. What is his name?

QUESTION 10
In *Stew-Roids*, which unlikely girl decides to date Chris because she's 'dated all the popular boys'?

QUESTION 11
In *Road to the Multiverse*, what does Chris win at the fair?

QUESTION 12
In *Stu and Stewie's Excellent Adventure*, a future Chris is married to an over-bearing woman, Vanessa. What is Chris's job?

QUESTION 13
In the opening credits of *The Family Goy* episode, which superhero is Chris?

QUESTION 14
Lois has a newspaper clipping of the time that Chris was born, it reads: "Local woman gives birth to a..." what?

QUESTION 15
Is Chris the oldest, middle or youngest child of the Griffins?

QUESTION 16
Who voices Chris?

QUESTION 17
What is Chris's middle name?

QUESTION 18
What is the name of the chesty blonde teacher Chris falls in love with?

QUESTION 19
Chris has a recurring nightmare involving Meg, what is Meg doing in the nightmare?

QUESTION 20
In *You May Now Kiss the... Uh... Guy Who Receives*, Chris falls in love with a lovely Young Republican. What is her name?

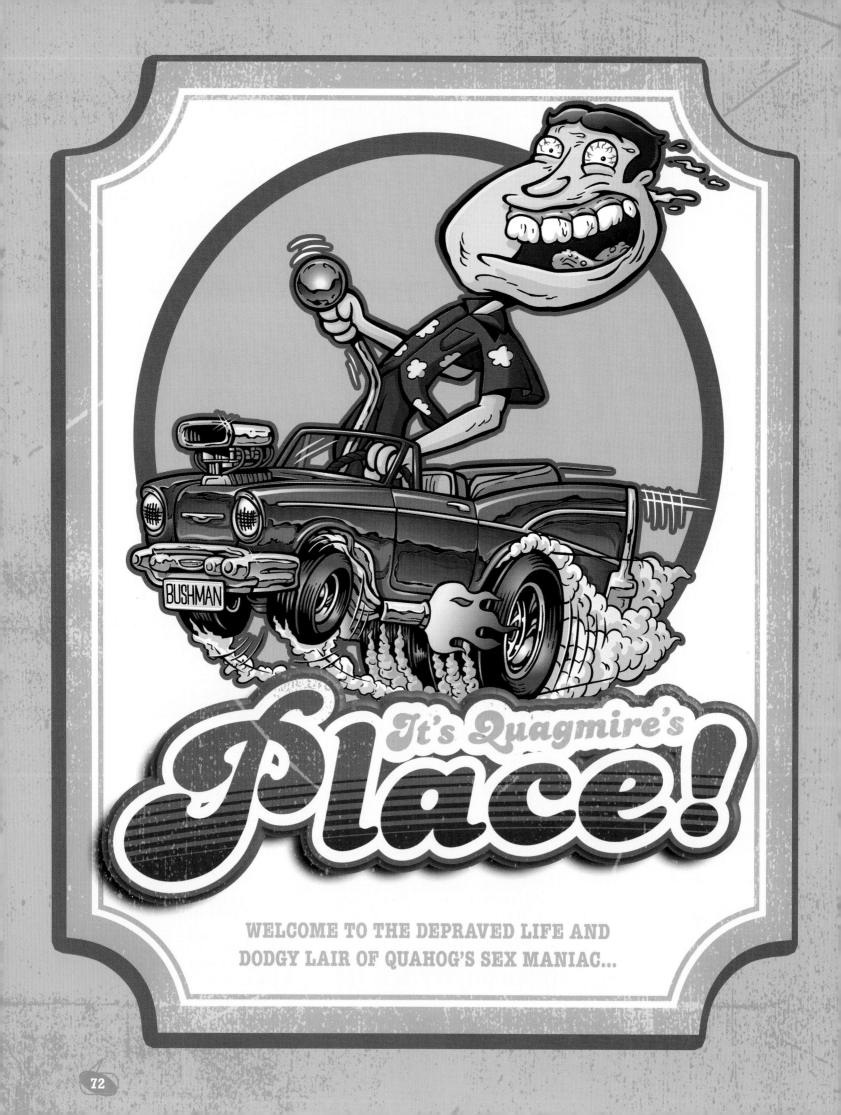

It's Quagmire's Place!

WELCOME TO THE DEPRAVED LIFE AND
DODGY LAIR OF QUAHOG'S SEX MANIAC...

"KEEPING AWAKE WHEN YOU'RE FULL OF ROHYPNOL TAKES EVERYTHING YOU'VE GOT... TAKE A BREAK FROM CONSCIOUSNESS AND TO YOU HE'LL DO THE LOT... YOU KNOW YOU SHOULDN'T GO, WHERE QUAGMIRE KNOWS YOUR NAME... AND HE'S ALWAYS GLAD HE CAME..."

Hey everybody, Cheers! And welcome to Quagmire's Place! It's true, Glenn Quagmire is an appalling human being who is still caught in the rat-pack era, a heartless sex hound who wouldn't think twice about giving a reach around to a spider monkey while reciting the Pledge of Allegiance, but more than that, he's got the worst chat-up lines around.

Join me in reciting some of his greatest hits: "If I could rearrange the alphabet, I would put 'U' and 'I' together", or "You must be the parking ticket, cos' you got fine written all over you" and "I don't want to get between you, or do I?"

He's a despicable man. When a woman asked him why he wanted to get married to her, he replied: "Hey, I only said that so you would Gigoogity my Gishmoigen!"

Yes, that's Quagmire! His Spooner Street lair has a discreetly hidden bed in nearly every part of the house, and he

needs it. He's been deflowering women across the world for over sixty years. Yes. Sixty Years! His secret? Carrots. Yes carrots: "Sometimes I grind them up into juice or just eat 'em raw... Or insert then anally. As long as I get 'em inside my body somehow."

Quagmire is not completely inhuman – he volunteers at a soup kitchen, is protective of his deaf brother and his sister ➡

IT'S QUAGMIRE!

Quagmire even has his own theme song!

♫ HE'S QUAGMIRE, QUAGMIRE
YOU NEVER REALLY KNOW WHAT HE'S GONNA DO NEXT
HE'S QUAGMIRE, QUAGMIRE
GIGGITY GIGGITY GIGGITY GIGGITY, LET'S HAVE SEX! ♫

Who didn't enjoy the song at the fancy dinner party where Quagmire stripped down to his underwear and danced upon the table? Or the funeral for the young woman who died a virgin where he popped out of the coffin in his underwear and danced off screen? You never know which injudicious place Quagmire will pop up next with his tailpenis and his tongue hanging way down...

IT'S QUAGMIRE'S PLACE!

Harriet from being beaten by her abusive boyfriend. He's also fallen in love a couple of times too – with Cheryl Tiegs, James the cat and his daughter Anna Leigh.

You know, maybe we're giving the guy a hard time? It could have been very different for Glenn. When Peter won Wheel of Fortune and a week of free maid service from Joan, Quagmire fell for the woman. If only he hadn't seen Lois' boob hanging out... But then what guy hasn't wanted to jump all over Lois after seeing the merest silhouette of her nipple on a cold and frosty morning?

You know, Quagmire loved Cheryl Tiegs. Really loved her. He often says he is just trying to fill the hole she left by having anonymous sex.

He has Lois's picture on the inside of his closet door, you know. He was even

arrested for peeping on Lois in the girls' bathroom.

James the cat? He loved that little ball of fur and matted faeces but James came to a terrible end. When Glenn went to Vermont to buy a present for James, Peter, Cleveland and Brian, attempted to shave James as a prank - it slightly back-fired when Peter accidentally stabbed the cat. The moral of the story is never play with scissors.

Unless you're opponent has gone paper, then you can go scissors. If they've gone rock, the scissors is a no-no. Like we said.

Quagmire's not a morning person. When a one-night stand, over breakfast, asked him what he did for a living he uttered those immortal words: "I have a question for you, too. Why are you still here?"

And it's not just his words

AUCTIONEER: **We open today's bidding with this pair of panties confiscated from a prostitute.**

QUAGMIRE: **Fifty bucks.**

AUCTIONEER: **She had nine STDs.**

QUAGMIRE: **Forty-five bucks.**

AUCTIONEER: **And when we caught her she wet herself.**

QUAGMIRE: **Fifty bucks.**

HEY, HEY, WAIT A MINUTE, WAIT, WHOA! WHAT THE HELL? YOU'RE NOT THE SAME GIRAFFE FROM LAST NIGHT!

PETER: **If you could have any woman in the world, who would it be?**

QUAGMIRE: **Taylor Hanson.**

JOE SWANSON: **Taylor Hanson's a guy.**

QUAGMIRE: **You guys are yankin' me. 'Hey, let's put one over on old Quagmire.'**

PETER: **No, he's actually a guy, Quagmire.**

QUAGMIRE: **What? This is insane. That's impossible.**

QUAGMIRE: **Oh my God. Oh my God. Oh my God. Oh God. I've got all these magazines. Oh God. Oh God.**

WELCOME TO MIDNIGHT Q. TONIGHT WE'RE GONNA ENJOY THE SMOOTH JAZZ OF CHARLES MINGUS. NORMAN MAILER'S HERE TO READ AN EXCERPT FROM HIS LATEST BOOK. AND THEN WE ALSO HAVE A GIRL FROM OMAHA WHO'S HIDING A BANANA. WE'LL FIND OUT WHERE. GIGGITY GIGGITY. GIGGITY GOO. STICK AROUND.

that carry Quagmire's every dirty idea on the wind, it's his thoughts too. When Peter, Joe, Quagmire and Cleveland are checking out the surveillance equipment in their new police van, Peter turns it up too high and Quagmires thoughts begin to come through! "Damn this itches. I wonder who gave it to me. Probably that skank who needed a ride to the gas station. Last time I do somebody a favour. Oh God, they must have heard me. OH GOD, I can hear me!"

In some ways, Quagmire is actually a pretty Conservative guy, he's not really that into gay marriage or sex with transvestites. When Brian asks him to support gay marriage to help out his cousin Jasper, Quagmire tells

him simply this: "Ah, come on two halves can't make a hole without a hole. Giggity, giggity, gigity, giggity. Ooh, ee, ooh ah ah Ting Tang Walla Walla Bing Bang!!"

We know he wasn't crazy when his dad, Dan Quagmire, like his son a veteran of the United States Navy, became Ida. He would have even preferred for his Dad to be gay.

When Dan told him: "Son, I give you my word, I'm not gay." Glenn replied: "Oh thank god!"

His Dad told him: "But I am a woman trapped in a man's body, and while I'm in town, I plan to have a sex change." "Oh c'mon, just be gay?," a desperate Glenn replied.

You know while we're on the subject, a man wanting to become a woman? Isn't that really the dream of all clowns?

The make-up, the frilly shirts, the inability to drive a car, the scoffing of custard pies, obsession with shoes, always taking it in the ass from a man they call The Ringmaster... The evidence is all there... that's all we're saying. The Evidence. Is. All. There.

Transvestites? Quagmire's not exactly got a clean bill of health. What about the time Brian caught Quagmire on his way back from the Phillipines?

He sniffed his crotch and, with a nose more sensitive to changes in the atmosphere than Barbara Streisand, told him: "You're back from Manila, you had Lumpia for dinner, then you had sex with two Fillipino women... and a man."

That's Quagmire! ∎

STEWIE'S LABORATORY

HE'S ONE OF THE WORLD'S GREATEST INVENTORS — WELL, SORT OF! SO LET'S HAVE A LOOK AT SOME OF HIS AMAZING GADGETS... OR SHOULD THAT BE DISMAL FAILURES?

STEWIE'S WORLD DOMINATION TOUR

Welcome to Stewie's Laboratory - a place that has come to the rescue of the Griffins more often than an ill-conceived plot device. Join us as we take a look at the Good, the Bad and the Madonna of Stewie's inventions.

First up, let's take a look at the Mind Control Device that was used on a judge to save Peter from jail. A mind control device on a judge? What was it, a brown envelope stuffed full of unmarked notes? Nope.

Next, a Laser Gun, disguised as a sandwich? Stewie may have used it try and kill Lois but who hasn't had their life threatened by a sandwich every time they've eaten from a badly parked burger van?

Stewie has tried to control the world's weather and, at the same time, destroy broccoli. He developed a Carbonite Gun to freeze a security guard for a decade. But then, how would you really know the difference?

Stewie has used his Time Machine to move forward in time and avoid the pain of teething and a Hypnotic Control Device to harness the unholy size and strength of Chris. Surely the only thing you'd need to harness Chris's size is a Family Pack of Twinkees?

In another episode, the family finds Stewie's body-switching orb. Lois and Peter swap bodies. Peter squeezes Lois' boobs. Who'd a thought it?

Stewie invented a device to control the public. Like you're going to need that? Surely, all you need to control the masses is a healthy political majority, a subservient mainstream media and a plentiful supply of gin? Ho, Ho. That sure gives it to The Man.

Stewie tried to keep Lois and Peter from having another baby by creating a robotic version of Peter. Then he shrank a battle cruiser to the size of a cell and armed it with phaser cannons to battle Peter's sperm cells! He's also created a hovering machine to kill Lois and a smaller flamethrower.

In *Stewie Griffin: The Untold Story*, Stewie creates robot lookalikes of himself and Brian so he can leave Quahog and find his real father. Later, he creates a pair of skis with rockets with a large tea room and butler, so he can get his Rupert back. Pretty obvious which one is more useful there, huh? Darjeeling anyone?

There was also a time when Stewie used a computer simulation machine to see what it would be like if he killed Lois and took over the world. But when Stewie finds out his plans end in disaster he scraps the computer simulation.

Stewie created another time machine which Mort thought it was a restroom – they had to go rescue him from Nazi Germany. But you probably knew that, racist.

Using blueprints he received at a Star Trek convention, he made a transporter to beam the cast of Star Trek: The Next Generation into his room, to ask them a few questions: "Oh, F*&k you Michael, 15 years later and you're still going on about that?!"

There's the Multiverse machine, sure thing. But you know the best invention Stewie ever made? It's got to be Bitch Stewie and Bitch Brian. The baby created deformed clones of himself and Brian. Genius.

The best line of the whole invention world? Bitch Brian: "I sharpened a pencil in my bum and now I need a band-aid." Even Stewie couldn't make that up.

IF I CHOOSE TO MAKE STOOL IN MY PANTS RIGHT NOW, YOU'RE THE ONLY ONE HERE TO CHANGE ME.

SO, YOU THINK YOU KNOW... MEG GRIFFIN?

QUESTION 1

Who provided the voice of Meg in the first season?

QUESTION 2

Which celebrity took Meg's virginity?

QUESTION 3

What is the name of the school bully who makes Meg's life even more of a living hell than it normally is?

QUESTION 4

Which of Meg's classmates idolises Meg?

QUESTION 5

Before he was shipped off to Iraq, Meg briefly dated Joe's son. What was his name?

QUESTION 6

In *Peter's Daughter*, Meg goes into a coma, how?

THE MOST ANONYMOUS MEMBER OF THE GRIFFIN FAMILY, ERM, WHATS-HER-NAME IS, ERM, A GIRL. YEAH, DEFINITELY A GIRL. THOUGH SHE IS KINDA UGLY. I MEAN, SHE COULD BE LIKE AN AMERICAN VERSION OF A THAI LADYBOY. AN AMERICAN LADYBOY, LIKE SAY ASHTON KUTCHER, OR PINK. Y'KNOW? ANYWAYS, ANSWERING QUESTIONS ABOUT MEG MUST BE LIKE HAVING YOUR TOENAILS RIPPED OUT. BUT IF YOU WANT TO, WELL... WE CAN'T STOP YOU, CAN WE?

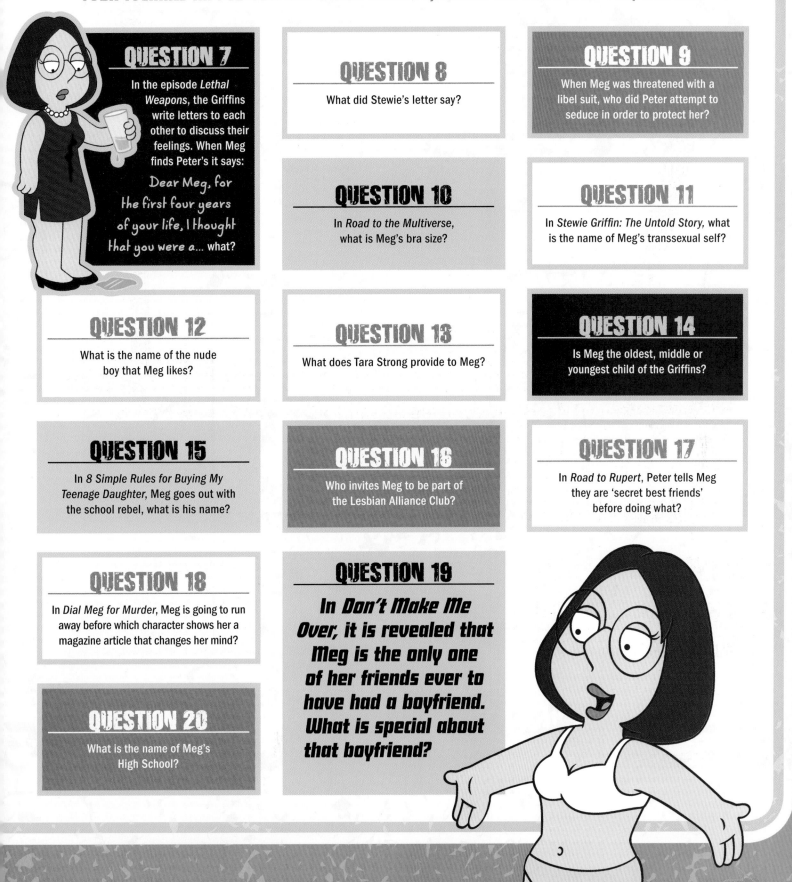

QUESTION 7

In the episode *Lethal Weapons*, the Griffins write letters to each other to discuss their feelings. When Meg finds Peter's it says:

Dear Meg, for the first four years of your life, I thought that you were a... what?

QUESTION 8

What did Stewie's letter say?

QUESTION 9

When Meg was threatened with a libel suit, who did Peter attempt to seduce in order to protect her?

QUESTION 10

In *Road to the Multiverse*, what is Meg's bra size?

QUESTION 11

In *Stewie Griffin: The Untold Story*, what is the name of Meg's transsexual self?

QUESTION 12

What is the name of the nude boy that Meg likes?

QUESTION 13

What does Tara Strong provide to Meg?

QUESTION 14

Is Meg the oldest, middle or youngest child of the Griffins?

QUESTION 15

In *8 Simple Rules for Buying My Teenage Daughter*, Meg goes out with the school rebel, what is his name?

QUESTION 16

Who invites Meg to be part of the Lesbian Alliance Club?

QUESTION 17

In *Road to Rupert*, Peter tells Meg they are 'secret best friends' before doing what?

QUESTION 18

In *Dial Meg for Murder*, Meg is going to run away before which character shows her a magazine article that changes her mind?

QUESTION 19

In *Don't Make Me Over*, it is revealed that Meg is the only one of her friends ever to have had a boyfriend. What is special about that boyfriend?

QUESTION 20

What is the name of Meg's High School?

ANIMAL GUY!

You know, Family Guy isn't beyond using the animal kingdom for cheap laughs. They're really good with animals, like roast potatoes and vegetables...

PIG UGLY

Need evidence? Look at the pig that Stewie introduced to Brian... Stewie: "Brian, look what I won." Brian: "Wow, what'd you win that for?" Stewie: "For having the best pig in the competition." Brian: "Wait, you bred a pig?" Stewie: "Sure did. Most genetically perfect one in the contest." Mutated Pig: "Oink!" Brian: "Oh my god!" Stewie: "Yeah, he's something, isn't he?" Brian: "Are those fists?!" Stewie: "Damn right! Show him pig!" Pig punches Brian in his face.

MONKEY BUSINESS

There's been Evil Monkey. You know why he was so evil? One day, he came home and found Mrs. Evil Monkey in bed with another monkey. He went bananas. Evil Monkey likes to relax by smoking a joint and listening to Foghat on vinyl through headphones on Chris' bed. Like a traffic warden, he points at people to strike up a conversation with them. He now lives in Jake Tucker's closet.

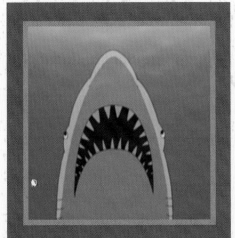

SHARK SNACK

Hey. I'ma eat y'all. I'ma eat that hairy leg. I'ma eat that one, too. Oh, I can see right up them shorts. I got a whole buncha rows of teeth to chew you with. Dun-na. Dun-na, Dun-na. Oh now wait a minute I did have a chubby kid on a raft earlier today. It's OK though, I been swimming a lot lately. MMM, yummy.

PARROT FASHION

In *Long John Peter*, Peter steals parrot Adrian Beaky from Dr. Jewish's vet office. After Joe says Peter looks like a pirate, hilarity, ahem, ensues. During Peter's battle with Shelley Boothbishop to rob him of his sugar cane, tobacco and spices, Adrian Beaky is seriously injured. A passing nurse steps on him and kicks him into a puddle of urine where his bowels release all over him before Dr. Jewish picks him up and throws him against a wall. Animal cruelty isn't Family Guy folks, it's Paris Hilton's dog. Just imagine how tired she gets carrying that little poop machine around.

IT'S HANDI-QUACKS!

One Day, 3 Ducks were crossing the road, goin' to get some soda. But they weren't looking where they were goin'. And the bus came along and hit them all. Now they're handicapped and... an... an... No... that's pretty much it! Handi-Quacks! And they never got their Sodaaaaaaaaa! (*From Foxy-y Lady*)

JASPER

So! Do you like Sex and the City? I'm not talking about the show. Ooooh I'm nasty! Honk Honk! Somebody ship me out to sea!

WILD LIFE!

"God, there is no better drummer than Rush's Neil Peart!" notes Chester Cheetah as he snorts up chopped Cheeto's. He smashes his fist through a glass table, with shards sticking out of his bloody hand and confirms that universal truth: "It ain't easy being cheesy."

DOG GONE...

The Griffins are true dog lovers. Think of all the lucky animals that have been welcomed to the show: There's Seabreeze who gave birth to part-canine, part-human offspring. There's Biscuit, Brian's mother who died, and was stuffed to become a couchside table. That's not to mention Barney who scratched away his nails, paws and lower part of his limbs when left listening to Public Service Broadcasting. Then there's Jasper, Brian's gay cousin, known for constantly making dirty jokes. Jasper is a gay dog who lives in LA and works at Club Med as a dance teacher and who appears in *Brian Does Hollywood*.

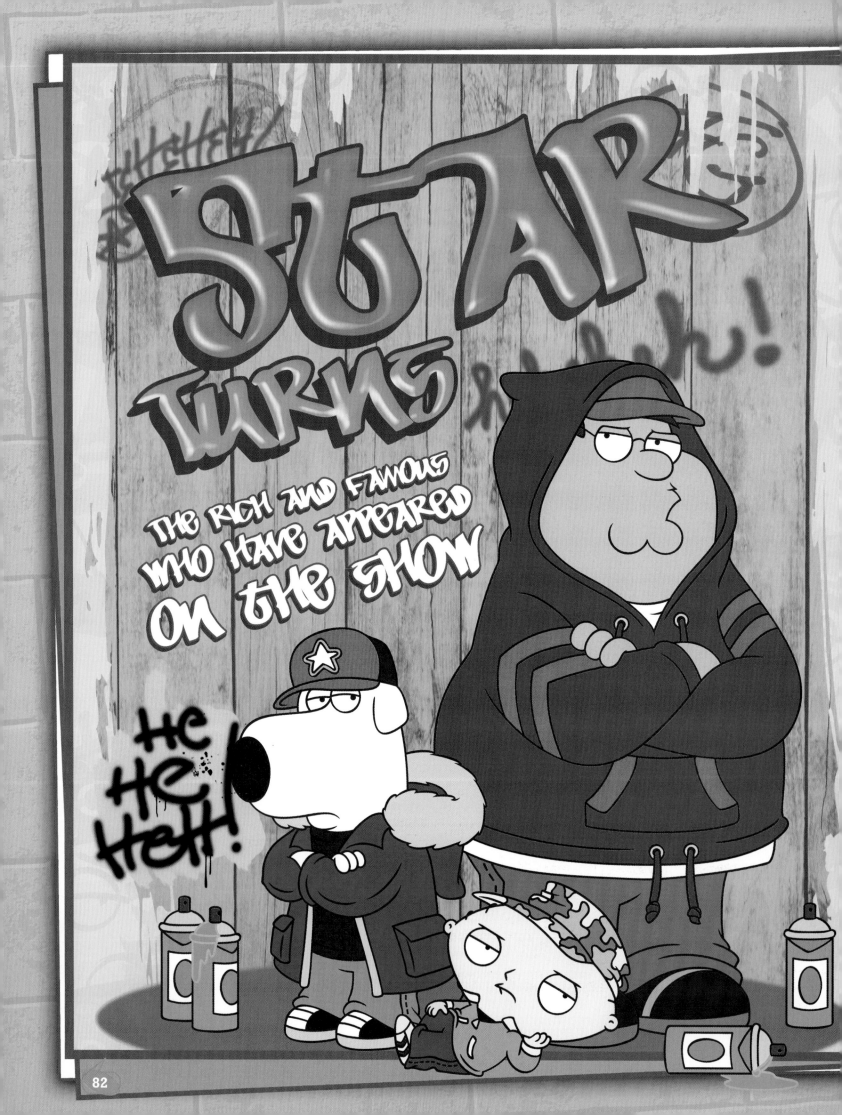

STAR TURNS

THE RICH AND FAMOUS WHO HAVE APPEARED ON THE SHOW

Family Guy is home to more than rabies and alcohol, it's home to good, honest celebrities and famous folk who have lied and cheated their way to the top and will stay there come hell, high water or the type of water that dislodges poo stains. Let's take a humorous trip back in time to see what those crazy losers have contributed to Spooner Street.

Adolf Hitler took a break from attempting to crush Europe to appear in *No Meals on Wheels*; Peter built a ScareJew in the form of Hitler to scare off Jewish Mort Goldman.

The Beatles appear in *Ready, Willing, and Disabled* as Stewie sets up a flashback by commenting that he'll do to Brian "what I did to John Lennon" – introducing Yoko Ono.

In *Stewie Kills Lois*, the lack of Ringo Starr's song writing abilities is exaggerated in a cut scene started by Brian. **Brian:** Great. This is even a bigger waste of time then Ringo's song writing. *(Cuts to a scene with*

Paul McCartney, George Harrison and John Lennon in a recording studio when Ringo Starr enters).
Ringo: Hey guys I wrote a song! **Paul:** Oh that's great! **John:** Oh good Ringo! **George:** Fantastic! **Paul:** *(Takes the song)* You know what? I'm gonna put it right here. *(hangs it up on a refrigerator)* Right on the refrigerator. That way we'll get to see it everyday. **Ringo:** All right!

Christina Aguilera used to have Peter as manager. In *Peter's Got Woods*, he tells her he despises everything about her: "You're pretty much offensive to all five senses."

When Aguilera says he's only mentioned four, Peter adds that her smell is so bad that he could taste it, like salty garbage. Aguilera licks herself and tells Peter: "Yeah, I totally taste it!"

In *Bill and Peter's Bogus Journey*, we see Jaws guy Roy Scheider's promotional poop video: Roy: "Hi, I'm Roy Scheider. And today we're going to learn to use the potty. Folks, say hi to my pal Hungry Hank. How's it going, Hank?" Hank: "I'm hungry for your poo. Don't make me starve."

In *Model Misbehaviour*, Peter says to Lois: "Lois, look at you! You

look like Britney Spears! Except not a fat guy."

And don't even get us started on that Federline douche.

Peter: "This is worse than that time when I was Kevin Federline's magic mirror."
(Flash to Kevin's apartment)
Federline: "Magic mirror, how can I look like a douchebag today?"

Peter: "Well Kevin, um first of all, I would say don't shave and don't shower."

Kevin: "Ok, I won't."

Peter: "And you just got out of bed, right?"

Kevin: "Yeah."

Peter: "Uh, I would say just go ahead and wear that tank top all day."

Kevin: "Um...ok."

Peter: "So let's see, we covered the hygiene, no collared shirts... um... oh! Don't forget to walk around with an undeserved sense of accomplishment."

Family Guy doesn't do discrimination. They offend black people too! Like the time Mayor West told anyone who wasn't listening: "We invited Reverend Jesse Jackson to open up our ceremonies with a prayer. Unfortunately he could not make it, so instead we have LaToya Jackson."

LaToya Jackson: "Rub a dub dub, thanks for the grub. Yea... God!"

And then there's any time George Takei says "Helllllllllloooooooooooooooo..." which freakin' floors us.

Bitter and twisted? Of course he is! Meet Carter Pewterschmidt.

GET OUT OF THIS HOUSE!

It's the Pewterschmidts!

Carter Pewterschmidt is a seventy-something with deep pockets and short hands who socializes with the likes of Bill Gates, Michael Eisner, and Ted Turner. He is a U.S. Steel supreme who once owned a greyhound, Seabreeze, which raced successfully before becoming impregnated by Turner.

He has a healthy addiction to sleeping pills and alcohol and an open marriage with his wife, Barbara, who he married for the money. He does not approve of gay marriage or voting rights for homosexuals: "Pah! Gay Marriage? Next thing we know, they'll want the vote!" And is never in the wrong: "Well, an apology is out of the question, and I'm assuming Rice Krispies is some kind of black slang for money, so here's $10,000."

Carter is a very senior member of the secret Skull and Bones Society where the most powerful men in the world are groomed for their futures: every president, every CEO.

Carter hates Peter. Moments after meeting him for the first time, Carter knocked him out with a bronze Etruscan statue and had him dumped naked in the middle of the Atlantic Ocean. Carter has also made Peter eat a pine cone, drink his blood and pushed him into a fire to retrieve

a five dollar bill at the bottom of a jar filled with salt and barbed wire.

Carter has very little attraction to his wife; he won't even look at the back of her head anymore. In fact, it is up to Peter to slake Barbara's sexual thirst. Why? Barbara and Peter are very much attracted to each other and almost had sex. Carter finds a naked Peter in his house… Carter: "Why are you naked in my house?" Peter: "Why aren't you?" Carter: "You're alright, Griffin."

Carter is a heartless man. When Peter took him to a lapdancing club for his first Bachelor Party and the girl started dancing in front of him, his first question? "When can I hit her?"

It is, however, possible to get to Carter's money, as Peter has proved when defeating his high tech security system with four locks: a combination lock, which can be cut round using Reese Witherspoon's chin; a voice identifier which Cleveland's

incredible impression skills get around; a penile identifier which Quagmire can just stick up and break; and the answer to the question: What is the most unattractive first name in the English language? The answer? Yeah, it's Keith.

Carter hates Barbara. Barbara Pewterschmidt once had an affair with Jackie Gleason, which traumatized their son, Patrick. Lois has no memory of Patrick in her childhood; she first discovered him in a folded-back Christmas picture. He was locked away in a mental institution after he suffered a breakdown and started killing people. He also has an imaginary wife named Marion.

Carol Pewterschmidt is the youngest Pewterschmidt child and lives in Texas with her ninth husband. The Griffin family briefly used her Texas home while waiting for rumours in Quahog that Stewie was possessed to blow over. Peter makes dirty phone calls to Carol while drunk. Carol's un-named son was delivered by Peter who almost cut off his penis when mistaking his newborn nephew for a girl with a tail.

Marguerite Pewterschmidt, Lois' great aunt, owned Cherrywood Manor in Newport, America's first presidential whorehouse. Ancestor Silas Pewterschmidt bartered with Native Americans by holding a knife to a baby's throat, sparing its life in exchange for maize.

NOW GET OUT!

SO, YOU THINK YOU KNOW...
STEWIE GRIFFIN?

QUESTION 1
What is the name of Stewie's half brother and arch-rival?

QUESTION 2
What is the name of Stewie's favourite teddy bear?

QUESTION 3
Who does Stewie marry and then kill by burning down a cardboard house with her inside?

QUESTION 4
Seth MacFarlane describes Stewie as being inspired by a famous English actor, what is his name?

QUESTION 5
What is the name of Stewie's favourite English children's Television Programme?

QUESTION 6
In *No Chris Left Behind*, which instrument does Stewie play at Chris while following him because he's fat?

THIS INVENTIVE, WISE-CRACKING TOT IS HELL-BENT ON WORLD DOMINATION (AND FINDING A PERFECTLY SNUG FITTING PAIR OF JEANS). BRIAN ASIDE, THE GRIFFINS LARGELY IGNORE STEWIE'S RAMBLINGS AT THEIR PERIL! PROVE THAT YOU HAVE NOT IGNORED THE CHOSEN ONE BY ANSWERING THE QUESTIONS BELOW. YOU MIGHT WANT TO SHINE A LAMP IN YOUR OWN FACE FOR THE FULL INTERROGATIVE EFFECT...

QUESTION 7
In the episode *Deep Throats*, what does Stewie ask Brian to shave?

QUESTION 8
In *Ocean's Three and a Half*, which girl does Stewie fall madly, deeply in love with?

QUESTION 9
Stewie has a secret lair in a large room hidden behind his bedroom wall, how does it open?

QUESTION 10
What is Stewie's email address?

QUESTION 11
What is Stewie's middle name?

QUESTION 12
Stewie has been stuck on the same age since season one. How old is he?

QUESTION 13
In the first eight seasons, Stewie and Brian have done five 'Road' movies, can you name them?

QUESTION 14
In '*Stewie Kills Lois*', the poster promoting the episode is a parody of which Hollywood blockbuster?

QUESTION 15
In *Quagmire's Baby*, what is the name of Stewie's clone?

QUESTION 16
When Stewie achieves global domination, what does he want to be called?

QUESTION 17
What is Stewie's favourite bedtime story?

QUESTION 18
In *Emission Impossible*, Stewie shrinks himself to go inside Peter's body and kill all his sperm. How does he escape from Peter's body?

QUESTION 19
In *To Love and Die in Dixie*, Stewie goes to Bumblescum and sets up a Hillbilly Jug Band, what was it called?

QUESTION 20
What was Stewie's first invention, which featured in *Family Guy's* first episode, *Death Has a Shadow*?

HEY, IT'S {HERBERT!}

YOUR GUIDE TO THE GRIFFINS' STRANGE NEIGHBOUR...

Herbert is Family Guy's friendly neighbourhood paedophile who lives just down the street from the Griffin family and, understandably, lusts after the young, athletic Chris.

The retired Army Veteran, and an Elder Member of the Skull and Bones Society, Herbert ambles towards his prey with a heart of gold and a head of ill-intention..

He's snuck into Chris' room late at night to paint his sleeping portrait, tried to seduce a Jockey, mistaking it for a child, attempted to snare children in butterfly nets and regularly dresses up as the Evil Queen.

In *Big Man on Hippocampus*, Chris, running down the street naked, believes he's invisible, to which an off-screen Herbert replies: "Oh, no you're not. Hot diggety!!"

In *Dial Meg for Murder* he bought popsicles, roofies and a mallet at Mort's Pharmacy. When asked why he was buying the kit, he replied: "To build a birdhouse for a rare African bird called Nunyabusiness!"

In *April in Quahog*, when the world was going to an end, wearing only his underwear, he told Chris: "Seems like I have run out of waitin' time." And in *Stewie Griffin: The Untold Story*, during the intermission, he is heard asking: "Chris do you have a shower scene? Or do I have to keep dreamin'?"

Herbert is keen on recycling. In *Road to Rupert* he patiently stands in line at the Griffin's garage sale. He asks Chris if he is selling any clothes he wore in the summer. When Chris tells Herbert that all he has fitting that description is a pair of shorts, Herbert exclaims: "Sweet Jesus!"

He's a committed member of the community, always looking to help out. In *Play It Again Brian*, Peter and Lois hire Herbert to babysit because he's 'spent time watchin' children'. After failing to give Chris a bath, he reads his own version of Peter and the Wolf as a bedtime story: "... and they told Peter to stay away from the wolf. But he didn't listen to them... cause he's his own man. And he knew that sometimes the things that seem the most dangerous turn out to be the most fun!" before quietly sleeping at the end of Chris' bed.

UNDRESSING HERBERT

Herbert was based on a whistley voiced retired old man who Mike Henry pushed groceries with while at High School.

Herbert was originally going to be a creepy school bus driver that Chris was afraid to go near, or an ice cream man.

Before Herbert made his first appearance on the show, Mike Henry would use the voice to motivate stalled writers.

JOE'S BEST PARTS

Part man, part wheel, part violent temper, Ladies and Gentlemen, please allow us to introduce a man apart – Mr. Joe Swanson. Actually Joe is a bit of a bad ass. That doesn't mean he keeps pooping himself, though he does. It means he's pretty tough, like Pink.

Actually, while we're here, doesn't it make you wonder? How come Herbert is still prowling the neighbourhood? Must be because he's pretty funny. What with that whistley voice and threat to the virginity of minors. Ho Hum.

Joe became paraplegic after falling from an orphanage roof while attempting to apprehend The Grinch who was stealing Christmas presents. You know who else steals Christmas presents? David Hasselhoff. It's trueeeeee….

Joe is a macho man, he's a rough tough mutha who'll shoot down a brother quicker than you can say Rodney King. He's like the ultimate cop: take Starsky's cardigan, Magnum's moustache, Poirot's bad breath and Sherlock Holmes' air of sexual ambiguity.

Joe falls out of his chair and is about to fall into the sewer when Lois catches him.

Lois: I can't hold on much longer!

Joe: Lois, pretend I'm one of your children! (Joe starts to slip)

Joe: Not Meg!

★ ★ ★ ★

Joe: Maybe Peter took the trophy, he wanted it all along.

Peter: I couldn't have taken it, I was too busy breakin' into Joe's garage stealin' his ladder so I could steal the trophy tonight!

Lois: Peter!

Peter: What? It's a ladder, he can't use it. It's like takin' a watch off a dead guy.

★ ★ ★ ★

Cleveland: I must say, I do feel a strange satisfaction watchin' the black ball topple all those self-righteous white pins.

Joe: Can't blame 'em for being self-righteous, the black ball's in their neighbourhood uninvited.

Cleveland: The black ball's done nothing wrong.

Joe: If the black ball's innocent it has nothing to fear.

Okay, so Joe might have a temper shorter than an albino's dance card but he's a man who won't let his disability stand in his way. Huh, get it?

He once entered and won the decathlon in the Special People's Games, became a sports celebrity, won huge endorsements and had an ABC special made about him, but was he happy? Of course he was happy. He was happier than the time the Little Mermaid discovered mammalian reproduction.

Joe is a devoted husband and father to Susie and the now sadly departed Kevin. Like any decent American, before Kevin's death, Joe pushed him right to the limit. The first time Kevin beat Joe in a competition, Joe gave him a small congratulatory punch, followed by a few more, then everything got a little hazy and Kevin had to go and live with a foster family for a while.

Joe has tried many times to regain his ability to walk. He has gotten new legs after Peter ate them (Joe and Peter were starving while floating on a raft made of blow-up sex dolls). Unfortunately, the new legs that Joe got were from a guy who was also paralysed.

You know, ultimately, Joe is exactly as his friends would like him. When he underwent a successful leg transplant, Peter, Glenn, Cleveland and Joe's wife became annoyed by the new arrogant, competitive, mobile Joe. He just wasn't himself any more!

The guys tried to beat Joe in the spine so he became paralysed again. And Bonnie Swanson, Joe's long-suffering wife, who has never been truly satisfied as a woman since Joe's accident, decided to shoot him in the spine with a gun. She missed but caught him a few times with some bullets.

Eventually Joe took the gun and shot out his own spine – no backbone that guy.

QUICK, RUN! It's Joe!

OR, ON SECOND THOUGHT, HANG AROUND AND LEARN SOMETHING ABOUT THE GUY...

WHAT YOU DON'T KNOW ABOUT
FAMILY GUY

Hey, you think you know it all? Sat there reading and giggling once every 45 pages? Well, here's some stuff you probably don't know smarty pants. And that's not to be confused with farty pants. See what we did there?

William H. Macy originally auditioned for the role of Brian.

Quagmire was Jack the Ripper in a previous life.

When the show was cancelled a second time, in 2003, there was an online petition with over 100,000 names on it to save the show.

Family Guy was the first programme to be resurrected on TV after a boom in DVD sales. In went off air in 2002 but returned in 2004.

Family Guy is banned in Indonesia, Taiwan, Vietnam, Iran, South Korea, South Africa and Malaysia.

'TO LIVE AND DIE IN DIXIE' WAS WAYLON JENNINGS' LAST ROLE BEFORE HE DIED.

American right-wing talk-show host Rush Limbaugh and former President George Bush's strategist Karl Rove were handed appearances in Family Guy. Programme creator Seth MacFarlane said it was because the show was "written by liberals" and he wanted to give Republicans a voice.

Every episode includes at least one instance of one character saying 'What the hell...'

CHRIS LOST HIS EARRING IN SERIES THREE.

On the morning of September 11, 2001, Seth MacFarlane was booked on American Airlines Flight 11 to fly from Boston to LA. His travel agent, however, mixed up the departure time and he arrived at Logan Airport 30 minutes late. Flight 11 crashed into the North Tower of the World Trade Center.

Brian drinks Martinis, Pawtucket Patriot Ale, Jack Daniels, Jagermeister and Mojitos.

Seth MacFarlane decided that Brian would be able to understand Stewie. Other adults understand Stewie but ignore whatever he says because he is a baby.

Quahog is modelled on Cranston, Rhode Island.

FAMILY GUY IS CONTRACTED TO MAKE NEW EPISODES UNTIL AT LEAST 2012.

According to Mayor West, Quahog was founded by a sailor of a boat bound for New York who was thrown overboard for his loquaciousness. A magical clam rescued him and brought him to shore and together they founded the town. Peter states that Quahog was founded by his ancestor Griffin Peterson.

Family Guy offshoot, 'The Cleveland Show' includes Cleveland's new wife, Donna. There'll also be a couple of step-siblings for Cleveland Jnr.: Donna's 16-year-old daughter, Roberta and her 5-year-old son, Rallo. Kanye West will provide the voice for one of Cleveland's son's soccer rivals, Kenny West.

A Quahog is a type of clam.

In 2009, Family Guy was nominated for an Emmy for 'Outstanding Comedy Series', becoming the first animated programme to be nominated in this category since The Flintstones in 1961.

The first episode of Family Guy, *Death Has A Shadow*, was viewed by more than 22 million homes. Brian sits down like a dog in this episode. Later on, he sits like a human.

Glen Quagmire drives a 1957 Chevy Bel Air Convertible.

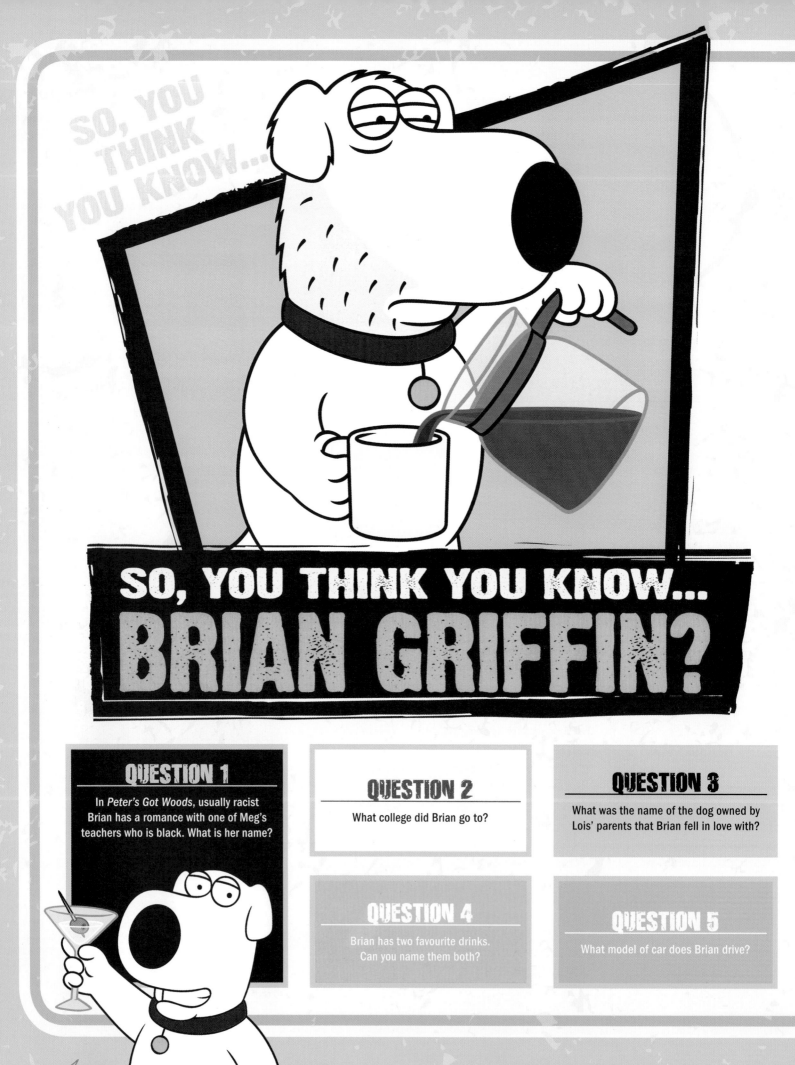

SO, YOU THINK YOU KNOW... BRIAN GRIFFIN?

QUESTION 1

In *Peter's Got Woods*, usually racist Brian has a romance with one of Meg's teachers who is black. What is her name?

QUESTION 2

What college did Brian go to?

QUESTION 3

What was the name of the dog owned by Lois' parents that Brian fell in love with?

QUESTION 4

Brian has two favourite drinks. Can you name them both?

QUESTION 5

What model of car does Brian drive?

PETER'S BEST FRIEND AND LOYAL COMPANION, BRIAN, A DIE HARD LIBERAL, ENJOYS MARTINIS, WRITING TERRIBLE FICTION AND BURYING THINGS IN THE YARD. EVEN THOUGH BRIAN IS A DOG WHO WEARS HIS HEART ON HIS SLEEVE, WHOSE EMOTIONS NEVER STRAY FAR FROM THE TRUTH, EQUALLY HE IS A MISUNDERSTOOD SOUL WHO CAN OFTEN BE FOUND CHASING HIS OWN TAIL. NOW HOW WELL DO YOU KNOW BRIAN'S TALE?

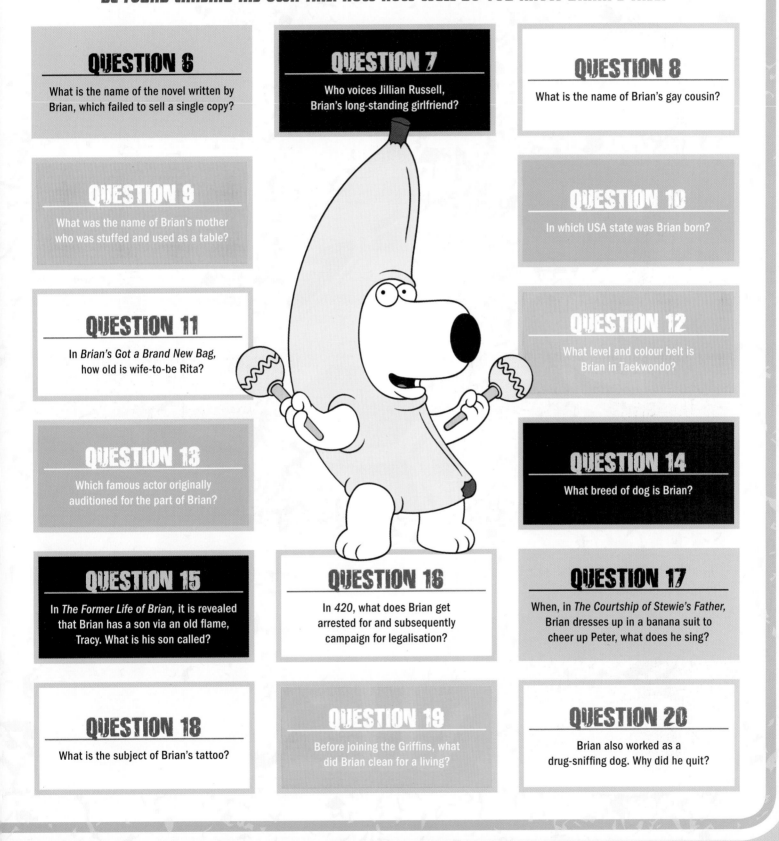

QUESTION 6
What is the name of the novel written by Brian, which failed to sell a single copy?

QUESTION 7
Who voices Jillian Russell, Brian's long-standing girlfriend?

QUESTION 8
What is the name of Brian's gay cousin?

QUESTION 9
What was the name of Brian's mother who was stuffed and used as a table?

QUESTION 10
In which USA state was Brian born?

QUESTION 11
In *Brian's Got a Brand New Bag*, how old is wife-to-be Rita?

QUESTION 12
What level and colour belt is Brian in Taekwondo?

QUESTION 13
Which famous actor originally auditioned for the part of Brian?

QUESTION 14
What breed of dog is Brian?

QUESTION 15
In *The Former Life of Brian*, it is revealed that Brian has a son via an old flame, Tracy. What is his son called?

QUESTION 16
In *420*, what does Brian get arrested for and subsequently campaign for legalisation?

QUESTION 17
When, in *The Courtship of Stewie's Father*, Brian dresses up in a banana suit to cheer up Peter, what does he sing?

QUESTION 18
What is the subject of Brian's tattoo?

QUESTION 19
Before joining the Griffins, what did Brian clean for a living?

QUESTION 20
Brian also worked as a drug-sniffing dog. Why did he quit?

While people all around the world die from starvation, persecution and super-sized fast food, join us for highlights from Family Guy Season Freakin' Eight!

Using a rotating dartboard, a brown paper bag, an orange, sleeping pills, half bottle of tequila and a life-time of tears, we have carefully selected our favourite eight episodes. But before we get to those, here are the also rans – the Jermaine Jacksons, the Alan Osmonds, the Esther Waltons…

Despite thinking it's more important than a dwarf amongst midgets, *Family Goy* didn't make it. In *Family Goy*, Quagmire discovers internet porn for the first time. Pretty obvious plot point, but let's roll with it… "What do you mean Internet porn? I'm not really a computer guy. You mean that crappy dial-up thing that's a pain in the ass? No I don't use the damn Internet. I thought that was for nerds?" Later, Quagmire opens the door to get his mail…. Peter: "Quagmire? There ya are, nobody's seen you in days." Quagmire seems exhausted. "Hey, Peter. I've just been, uh… checking out some of that Internet porn." Peter: "You okay?" Quagmire: "Yeah, yeah, I'm good, I'm good… I'm just gonna… go check my mail over there." Lifts his left arm to point to the mailbox, revealing that it is incredibly muscular. Peter: "You been liftin' weights?" Quagmire: "Uh, no… No, no… I don't think so… no, um, uh, um, I'm-I'm sorry, Peter… I gotta, I gotta get back."

The worst part of this story? The very worst part? It's not the innuendo that Quagmire's been jacking off, that he's been locked away for days doing the unspeakable to the unmentionable, that he's been scouring the darkest recesses of the web. It's that he's a lefty. Look again, it's heinous. They walk freely amongst us people. A freedom they take for granted.

In *Brian's Got A Brand New Bag*, Brian dates an older woman, Rita, while Peter, inspired by *Road House*, believes everything can be solved with violence. Peter: "Oh my god, Road House. I want to buy this." Shop assistant: "Great, and as a bonus I'll throw in *What Dreams May Come*." Peter: "No thank you." Assistant: "No charge." Peter: "If that DVD even touches *Road House*, I will kill you.*"

In *Hannah Banana,* Stewie meets Hannah Montana while Chris tries to prove that the Evil Monkey exists. After Chris finally catches Evil Monkey, Evil Monkey and Peter are sat chatting in the front room. Chris walks in the room and shouts angrily: "Well, I'm glad you guys are having such a great time with that evil thing that tortured me for years! Dad, I thought you were going to help me with my book report." Peter: "Chris, there's a monkey here. And I just fed him a whole bag of Subway sandwiches. In a couple hours, we are going to sit around and throw his soft bread stool at each other. Now,

you are welcome to be a part of that. Or not. I'm just telling you what's gonna happen."

Dog Gone sees Brian kill a dog in a road accident, but no-one cares... Brian: "I just can't believe our society actually values the life of a dog less than that of a human. It's infuriating." Stewie: "That is infuriating. Maybe you should go bark at a tree and chew on your balls for an hour." Meanwhile, Lois is tired of Peter's mess, so

she hires Consuela... Consuela gets into bed next to Chris and hogs all the covers. Chris: "Can I get I get some covers over here?" Consuela: "No... No.... your fat keep you warm."

The reason *Business Guy* didn't make it is because it's a bigger downer than a German bedtime story... Zere vunce vas a boy who liked to suck his thumbs. His musser asked him to stop but he vouldn't. So she cut off his thumbs. Now he has no thumbs. Gutt night.

In a not-very-memorable episode, *The Big Man on Hippocampus,* Peter loses his memory.

Dial Meg for Murder, now there's a doozy. Best bit? Meg comes home from jail and wants to establish some sort of pecking order in the Griffin Hen House… Meg: "First question who's the biggest, toughest guy in this house?" Peter: "Well, I don't like to toot my own horn, but I believe I hold the distinction…" Meg punches Peter off the couch with a lamp, grabs his head and starts punching and kicking his face. Meg drags Peter to the stairs and jumps on his head which breaks all his teeth in his upper jaw. Meg: "My house now, bitch! Now who's the funniest?" Peter lifts his hand up. "I know my way around a joke." Meg kicks and stomps on Peter's face. Chris: "For God's sake, Dad, have some humility! It'll save your life!"

In *Peter-assment*, Peter's boss, Angela, understandably falls in lust with Peter. But before that, Peter tries his hand at video journalism. Peter: "Hey, Chris, look, is that Richard Dreyfuss?" Dreyfuss: "Oh, for crying out loud." He gets up and goes to the men's room… Peter: "Oh, you going to the bathroom? You gonna have a close encounter of the turd kind? Hey, I think you're gonna need a bigger boat. These jokes are for you, Peter, when you watch this tape in the future. Hi, future Peter. I'm gonna plant a tree for you when I get home. Look outside and you'll see a grown tree." Cut to

an older Peter watching a video in the living room. Past Peter on the video: "I'm going to plant a tree for you when I get home. Look outside and you'll see a grown tree." Future Peter looks out and sees a grown tree! Past Peter on the video: "Now look at your hand. It's just a nub, 'cause I'm gonna cut off all the fingers." Future Peter looks at his fingerless right hand. Future Peter: "Oh, yeah, past Peter? Well, two can play that game." Future Peter pulls out a machete and cuts his right arm off. "Take that. Uh, wait a minute."

In *Brian Griffin's House of Payne*, Brian sees a pilot of his show 'What I Learned on Jefferson Street' made. The best bit? Peter pulls a leg from the turkey. Peter: "Oh, oh, look, Lois, wishbone. Okay, ready? One, two, three." Peter gets the bigger

piece and makes a wish. Peter: "Yes! I got five seconds." Peter runs out of the room, returns, nails his chair to the ground and sits on it as everything, including his family, smashes into the ceiling! Peter: "Hah! No gravity!"

April in Quahog sees Quahog suffer a black hole hoax and Peter called up for Jury Duty. Peter: "Jury duty sounds boring. I'm gonna get myself kicked out. Just like I got kicked out of Coldplay." Peter with Coldplay: "Guys, guys, I got an idea! How 'bout we do a song that's not whiny bull poo?"

So there you are, a quick look at the shows that didn't make our Season Eight highlights. Here's the ones – hand chosen – that you can count on your fingers, if you've got only eight fingers…

While Family Guy Season Eight viewers will have tuned in for the compelling characters, witty wordplay, awesome asides and any alternative alliteration, Season Eight contains some of Brian & Stewie's best work.

Stewie and Brian have come a long, long way since Season One's *Death Has A Shadow*. They've survived Stewie's criticism of Brian's lack of writing action...

 Stewie: "How you uh, how you comin' on that novel you're working on? Huh? Gotta a big, uh, big stack of papers there? Gotta, gotta nice litte story you're working on there? Your big novel you've been working on for three years? Huh? Gotta, gotta compelling protaganist? Yeah? Gotta obstacle for him to overcome? Huh? Gotta story brewing there? Working on, working on that for quite some time? Huh? (voice getting higher pitched) Yea, talking about that 3 years ago. Been working on that the whole time? Nice little narrative? Beginning, middle, and end? Some friends become enemies, some enemies become friends? At the end your main character is richer from the experience? Yeah? Yeah? (voice returns to normal) No, no, you deserve some time off."

Makes you wonder why Cleveland gets his own show while they play second fiddle to The Fat Man, doesn't it? As Brian might say, it's positive action gone mad.

Park your anger, control your fury and enjoy these pages that have been put together to let you, dear reader, enjoy the best lines from Stewie and Brian from Season Eight.

First up, please join us to enjoy some of the finest performances in American television as we re-live this legendary scene from *Hannah Banana*...

 Stewie: "My God, I can't believe she's an android. Do you think we should tell someone or do something?"

 Brian: "Well, we could do something."

 Stewie: "Like what?"

 Brian: "Well, look at her. She dances like a real girl. She moves like a real girl."

 **Stewie:** "Yeah?"

 Brian: "Do you think she does other stuff like a real girl? You know, if you reprogrammed her?"

 Stewie: "Brian, that's sick! She's 16!"

 Brian: "I'm eight."

 Stewie: "All right, I'll see what I can do."

You know that Miley Cirus was alright? She was alright, y'know?

Right, here's the scene from *Quagmire's Baby*, the one where Brian walks into the bathroom and Stewie and Bitch Stewie are taking a nice, hot relaxing bath...

 Brian: "Oh, sorry, didn't realise somebody was in here. What the hell?"

Stewie: "Oh, hello, Brian."

Bitch Stewie: "Oh, there's your friend, Brian! Hey, Brian! I sure did enjoy talking to you the other day! I'm just making sure Stewie

The Brian & Stewie Show

Bitch Stewie: "I told him I did the poos even though you did the poos, Stewie. Did I do good, Stewie?"

 Stewie: "That was very correct of you, Bitch Stewie. You're a good helper."

And they say the art of comedy is dying? Has anyone ever actually heard Sarah Palin trying to spell necessary? Here's the scene from *Go, Stewie Go* where Stewie dresses as Karina. Brian is at the Park Barrington Hotel, having a drink when Karina walks in...

Karina: "Hello there."

 Brian: "Hello."

Karina: "Um, I'm new in town and I'm awfully lonely. I'm wondering if you wouldn't mind buying me a drink."

 Brian: "Well, that'd be my pleasure. And maybe later I can show you some of the local points of interest. There's one right below the table."

Karina: "Oh, my, you're very bold."

 Brian: "Well, when your lifespan is 13 years, you gotta be direct."

Karina: "Lucky for you, I like bold men. Karina, Karina Smirnoff."

is nice and clean for his trip to the playground this afternoon."

 Stewie: "We had a little bit of a problem earlier because Bitch Stewie was stooling in the tub, wasn't he?"

Bitch Stewie: "I did some poos. I did some poos. I didn't mean to."

 Stewie: "But we've rectified that now, and everything's fine."

 Brian: "This is really weird. I mean, it's one thing to

have him help you out with a busy schedule. It's another thing to let him wash your back."

 Stewie: "Well, he does more than that, Brian. Bitch Stewie, give me a bubble beard."

 Stewie: "Look at me, I'm George Bernard Shaw."

Bitch Stewie: "That's awful funny, Stewie! I don't know who George Bernard Shaw is, but you look like an old Stewie, Stewie."

Brian: "Enjoy your weird bath."

Brian: "Brian, Brian Steel."

Karina: "Ooh, good heavens!"

Brian: "Man, your accent is sexy."

Karina: "Oh, this is all moving very quickly. I'm afraid I'm a little light-headed. You must think I'm a fool."

Brian: "I'm, I'm sorry, I didn't mean to come on too strong."

Karina: "Oh, that's alright. I've been missing a man's touch, these many months."

Brian: "And I've been missing a woman's touch."

(Brian moves Stewie/ Karina's hand to his crotch.

Stewie: "Brian, Brian, it's me, Stewie! Oh, my God, that was hilarious! You really fell for it! I… I… was like, Is he gonna fall for this? And then when you did, I was like, I guess I should see how far I can take it 'cause you know it'll be funnier."

Brian: "I'm gonna kill you! Why are you dressed like that?!"

Stewie: "Uh, because I'm the star of Jolly Farm. Remember how they only needed little girls?"

Brian: "Oh, my God. I'm telling Lois."

Stewie: "You're not telling anybody, friend. No, no, you're gonna be my on-set guardian."

Brian: "You're out of your mind."

Stewie: "Brian, we both know I touched it. Now, if you'd like to keep that just between us, I suggest you sit back down and order me some chicken fingers."

Stewie: "See? We're having a nice time."

DEAR STUPID DOG,

I'VE GONE TO LIVE WITH THE CHILDREN ON JOLLY FARM. GOODBYE FOREVER.

Stewie

PS: I never got a chance to return that sweater Lois gave me for Christmas. Umm, I left the receipt on top of my bureau. I'm probably over the thirty-day return limit but umm… I'm sure if you make a fuss they'll at least give you a store credit or something. Umm… It's actually not a horrible sweater. It's… It's just I can't imagine when I would ever wear it you know? Oh and I also left a button on the bureau. Umm, I'm not sure what it goes to, but I can never bring myself to throw a button away. I know as soon as I do I'll find the garment it goes to and then it'll… Wait a minute, could it be from the sweater? Did that sweater have buttons? Hmm… Well I should wrap this up before I start to ramble. Again, goodbye forever.

PPS: You know, it might be a little chilly in London, I'm actually going to take the sweater.

SEASON EIGHT

HIGHLIGHT

Extra Large, Medium

During an (admittedly unlikely) Griffin family hike around a local forest, Chris and Stewie get lost chasing a butterfly.

Chris: "Stewie, look. A butterfly. Let's get it!" Stewie: "Uh, Chris, I don't think we should be leaving the trail." British Guy appears and catches the butterfly: "I shall put you in a glass box to display on Saint Trimmings Day." Chris: "Oh, British guys always capture my butterflies." British Guy: "Yes, and to add insult to injury, I shall present to you my fanny: Sir Chadwell Heath."

They are missing for days, which sends Lois frantic. Park Ranger: "We're still very optimistic that we're gonna find these kids, and we just want to urge everyone not to give up hope."

Joe: "All right, everyone, we are officially looking for corpses. Repeat, this is now a recovery effort. We are officially looking for corpses. So

let's get back out there, bring back those dead bodies."

Lois is so frantic she looks to a psychic medium to re-assure her that her boys are safe. They are eventually rescued by Bruce: "Jeffery! Jeffery, come back. It's gonna get dark soon! All this drama over a turkey burger?! Oh, you're not Jeffrey. You're that missing baby and boy. Jeffery! I found that missing baby and boy!"

Back in Quahog, Lois is obsessed by all things psychic – Brian poo poos the psychic world by getting Peter to cold read passers by.

Peter: "Excuse me, ma'am. I'm psychic, and I'm getting a strong feeling from you. Do you have a watch or clock that no longer works? I'm also sensing that you have a dead relative. Okay, uh, I'm sensing some other bad stuff. Hey, you don't want to hear the truth, don't come to the park."

Predictably, Peter has fooled himself into thinking he has ESP (and we don't mean extra

soiled pants) and starts performing to live crowds.

Peter: "Thank you. Thank you so much for coming. Thank... Hold on. I'm sensing something psychic. Ma'am, did you have a female relative who's passed on to the other side named, um, um... Polly? I said it first. I'm sensing a black guy over here. Is there a black guy? Yes, good, good. I'm sensing your infant daughter has earrings. I'm sensing a doctor in the audience. Where is the doctor? Okay. Your great grandmother is contacting me right now, and she wants to know (pulls his pants down revealing his butt with a rash on it) if this rash looks like it's going to go away. She says Bactine hurts. She wants something more soothing."

When Joe asks Peter to track down a missing person who has a bomb tied to him, his cover is blown.

Meanwhile, when Chris and Stewie were lost, Chris promised

CHRIS: "SHE'S SO SWEET. AND DOESN'T SHE HAVE THE MOST BEAUTIFUL EYES?"

STEWIE: "WELL, THE SPACING SEEMS A TAD OFF, BUT, YEAH, INDIVIDUALLY, THEY'RE NOT AWFUL. ALL RIGHT, I'M ON BOARD. GO TALK TO HER."

to ask out a school classmate with Down's Syndrome, Ellen.

Chris: "She's so sweet. And doesn't she have the most beautiful eyes?" Stewie: "Well, the spacing seems a tad off, but, yeah, individually, they're not awful. All right, I'm on board. Go talk to her." However, rather than fall for Ellen, Chris finds her rude and demanding.

Chris: "All right, that is it! I don't care how hot you are. I don't much like being treated this way. You know, I used to hear that people with Down's syndrome were different than the rest of us, but you're not. You're not different at all. You're just a bunch of assholes like everyone else!"

Stewie re-assures Chris: "Oh, she would have crushed your scrote into a diamond with her robot-strength hand. Come on, let's get out of here."

Jerome is the New Black

Peter, Joe and Quagmire are downing a few suds and catch an ad for the Rat Pack's Most Bigoted Songs... Drunk Old Injun! *The Drunk Old Injun squatting in his tepee, firewater keeping him warm...* Jewish Nose! *She's got a big beautiful Jewish nose and it's there two minutes early wherever she goes...* Chinaman's Chance! *And Mr. Chinaman say in his Chinaman way dinga linga longa chinga chonga chinga chong achoo...* Phew Stinky Frenchmen! *Paris is lovely and Nice sure is nice and Marseille is charming with Champagne on ice, but you stinky Frenchmen haven't a clue, stinky Frenchmen, Frog You!* Hey There, Fruity! *Hey there fruity, you can do my hair, Hey there fruity, don't touch me down there. Hey there fruity, you're gay and I don't approve...*

The trio decide they need a new friend to replace Cleveland... and he has to be black. Step forward Jerome, a big large black man with a voice like sexual chocolate and a beard like runny chocolate... "I got time for whatever I want, fool. My watch don't tell time, I tell it."

Peter introduces Jerome to Lois. The two used to date. Peter grows jealous and in a drunken state unintentionally burns down Jerome's house. Now without a place to live Jerome moves in with the Griffins. Jeesh, this is like a bad episode of Family Ties. Whose idea was this? Peter suspects Jerome and Lois will sleep together and drives his new big black friend out by dressing like the Ku Klux Klan. Eventually, Lois shows Peter the error of his ways, Peter apologises, Jerome accepts. Though at the end, Jerome tells Peter that while he didn't sleep with Lois but he did have lots of 'nasty-ass sex' with Meg. Peter doesn't care.

Meanwhile, in a plot twist twistier than a twist of lemon on a helter skelter, Brian discovers Quagmire hates him. Brian attempts to mend the relationship by taking Quagmire

out for steak. Eventually the reason why Quagmire hates Brian is finally revealed...

Quagmire: "Okay, I'll tell you. You are the worst person I know. You constantly hit on your best friend's wife. The man pays for your food and rescued you from certain death, and this is how you repay him? And to add insult to injury, you defecate all over his yard. And you're such a sponge. You pay for nothing. You always say: 'Oh, I'll get you later' but 'later' never comes. And what really bothers me is you pretend you're this deep guy who loves women for their souls when all you do is date bimbos. Yeah, I date women for their bodies but at least I'm honest about it. I don't buy them a copy of Catcher in the Rye and then lecture them with some seventh grade interpretation of how Holden Caulfield is some profound, intellectual. He wasn't! He was a spoiled brat! And that's why you like him so much – he's you! God, you're pretentious! And you delude yourself by thinking you're some great writer, even though you're terrible! You know,

"IN A PLOT TWIST TWISTIER THAN A TWIST OF LEMON ON A HELTER SKELTER, BRIAN DISCOVERS QUAGMIRE HATES HIM."

I should have known Cheryl Tiegs didn't write me that note. She would have known there's no 'a' in the word 'definite.' And I think what I hate most about you is your textbook liberal agenda, how we should 'legalise pot, man,' how big business is crushing the underclass, how homelessness is the biggest tragedy in America. Well, what have you done to help? I work down at the soup kitchen, Brian. Never seen you down there! You wanna help? Grab a ladle! And by the way, driving a Prius doesn't make you Jesus Christ! Oh, wait! You don't believe in Jesus Christ or any religion for that matter, because religion is for idiots! Well, who the hell are you to talk down to anyone? You failed college twice, which isn't nearly as bad as your failure as a father! How's that son of yours you never see? But you know what? I could forgive all of that, all of it, if you weren't such a bore! That's the worst of it, Brian. You're just a big, sad, alcoholic bore... Thanks for the stinking steak."

Brian returns home. He's been crying. Stewie allows him to sleep on the floor. Brian farts. Gotta love this show.

Quagmire's Baby

You know, since Cleveland left the show, it feels like there's a really big hole to fill. Cleveland's hole needs filling again and again and again. Over the course of Season Eight, thanks in no small part to Quagmire, the hole has become smaller and with it, the scenes have become tighter. Joe tried to fill that hole, but he's dead from the waist down. Nope, Quagmire is the man to fill Cleveland's hole, he's gotten so deep into that hole that I don't think he'll ever come out of it.

CAUTION: TOXIC FUMES

9n Quagmire's Baby, Peter buys a ham radio from Quagmire and communicates with Ronald Reagan. When he finds out it's a fake, Peter tries to take the radio back, but Quagmire won't have it... Peter: "Yeah, but you were Agamemnon with me during the sale. I just saw that word somewhere. I wanted to use it."

Quagmire and Peter see a baby in a basket by his door, with a note that reads: "Glen, this is your child. Next time use a condom, jerk." Now Quagmire has to take the baby... "Not really sure what I'm supposed to do with you. There's some frozen steaks in the freezer. Bathroom's down the hall to the right. Uh, if you ever come home and there's a tie on the door, it means I'm froggin' someone, so give me at least, uh, a

couple hours. You smoke?"

Quagmire just can't cut it, so Peter asks: "Have you considered abortion?" Quagmire suggests it's a bit too late for that. Peter replies: "Oh, don't let the press put the scare into you. Wade v. Boggs has not been overturned." Glen: "Yeah, but you can't really abort a live baby." Peter: "Ho, boy, they have got you... Glen, Glen. (whispers) Give her back to God."

Quagmire eventually decides to put Annaleigh up for adoption... "She'll be somewhere safe, right? Like, you're not going to put her with sand people, right?"

To celebrate, Peter, Quagmire and Joe visit the Fuzzy Clam strip joint club, as Peter so eloquently puts it: "This will be great, Quagmire. A nudie bar is the perfect way to celebrate your first night without a baby." Quagmire tells him: "Yeah, Peter, this is great. I feel like myself again. I'll tell ya, my life was so dominated by that baby. I'm glad she's gone."

But that's before Quagmire starts reminiscing about

❝ THIS WILL BE GREAT, QUAGMIRE. A NUDIE BAR IS THE PERFECT WAY TO CELEBRATE YOUR FIRST NIGHT WITHOUT A BABY. ❞

Annaleigh... "Heh. That stripper has a rash on her ass, just like Annaleigh used to get... And that other stripper's sitting on that guy's lap, just like Annaleigh used to do... And that stripper only has one tooth, just like Annaleigh... I think I might have made a terrible mistake!"

Quagmire tracks down Annaleigh and sees how happy she is with her new family... "She looks so happy. Almost like she belongs there. They look like a real family. I can't take her away from this."

As they walk away, Peter tells Quagmire: "You know, I got to tell you, I think you did a good thing." Quagmire replies... "Well, I guess I just realised it's not about me. This family is what's best for Annaleigh. This is her home now. I gotta let her go." Peter is proud of Quagmire. "Hey, who knows? Maybe I'll bump into her in 18 years... Did you really think I was going to change that much?"

SEASON EIGHT

HIGHLIGHT

Quagmire's Dad

Quagmire can't wait to show his dad to the guys. Dan Quagmire is a man with a huge reputation for a way with the ladies. Joe and Peter visit Quagmire's house and meet Lieutenant Commander Dan Quagmire, who asks to be introduced to the sound of 'These Boots Are Made For Walking' and for a cosmo. Can you see where this is going yet? Son proud of his father's sexual exploits, father is a little gay... Hmm... Peter and Joe catch on and start texting each other... Joe: "How gay is this guy?" Peter: "He's so ducking gay... Oh sorry, that's my spellcheck." Peter tells Lois that

Quagmire's dad is gay, but Lois is a little suspicious, asking Peter how he knows. "He had the complete DVD set of Sex and The City between his butt cheeks."

Peter tells Quagmire his father is gay. Quagmire is in denial. Peter and Lois are invited to a Naval Ball to celebrate the life of Dan. At the ball, Quagmire's Naval buddies can't wait to tell Quagmire what a swell guy his dad is... "it's great to see you back in your element tonight, surrounded by sea men... Hey, you Dan's boy? Your dad was very brave back in South East Asia, he flew supplies in, where others wouldn't dare to go. I can't tell you how many loads your dad took when I served with him. He'd walk into an army barracks and made every Private there feel important. Yeah, he just knew how to stroke those Privates... Everyday at rifle training, he'd help me clean my butt... If there was one man you wanted

in your hole, it was your dad."

Quagmire confronts his father, who tells him: "I'm not gay. But I am a woman trapped in a man's body and while I am in Quahog, I plan to have a sex change operation."

Quagmire asks Peter and Lois for advice, telling them his dad wants a sex change operation. Peter retorts: "Woah, I knew he was gay but I didn't think he was that gay!" Peter agrees to join Quagmire at the hospital for the operation but only if "anything he lops off we get to bring home to Brian". At the hospital Peter asks: "What're you gonna name it, huh? What're you gonna name your he/she father/mother?"

When Ida steps out of the operating theatre she is a beautiful blonde. At dinner later, Peter begins asking Ida about the surgery: "So Ida, you miss

" WHAT DO I CALL YOU? MY DAD WHO PEES SITTING DOWN, BUT CAN ALSO PALM A BASKETBALL?!"

your penis? So tell me about those knockers, is that just like implants or did they re-assign some ass-fat up there?" Quagmire storms out and rejects his father: "I don't even know what to call you...my friend who pees sitting down, but can also palm a basketball?!"

Meanwhile, Brian returns home after a book seminar and stops off at a hotel bar. He meets Ida. Brian and Ida talk, kiss and have sex in the hotel. Next morning, back at the ranch, he shows Peter and Lois his new love on his mobile. Peter and Lois crack up. Stewie tells Brian that Qaugmire's dad has had a sex change: "It's got to be a trainwreck down there, right? Just an absolute casserole of nonsense." Brian vomits when he realises who he has had sex with.

Ida returns to Quagmire's house to try and patch things up. Eventually, Ida gets around to telling him that she has met a man – Brian. Quagmire is livid, runs next door and beats seven shades of crap out of Brian: "Now lay there and die, you piece of crap!" After taking the pounding of three lifetimes, it is Brian who has the last word: "Hey, I made out with your dad."

[HIGHLIGHT]

SEASON EIGHT

Spies Reminiscent of Us

Peter starts using Cleveland's empty house to poop in (don't ask...).

Lois: "Peter, your breakfast is ready."
Peter: "Hang on. I'll be right back, Lois. I'm just going across the street."
Lois: "Peter, you can't keep using

Cleveland's bathroom!"
Peter: "Oh, my god! Yes I can! Cleveland's bathroom is the greatest discovery since fat women discovered Diet Coke."
(Fat woman drinks Diet Coke): "Now I can eat anything!
   Chevy Chase and Dan Ackroyd spoil Peter's stool-based

fun by moving into Cleveland's old house. Shortly after, Peter invites them over to dinner...
   Peter: "Can you believe it? We're eating with two of the three ghostbusters."
Chevy: "Actually, I wasn't in that."
   Peter: "Look at these guys, they can't take a compliment."

Stewie and Brian discover Chase/Ackroyd's secret underground bunker beneath Cleveland's place...

Ackroyd: "Welcome to D.U.M.P. – Deep Underground Military Protection Facility."
Stewie: "Wouldn't that be D.U.M.P.F.?"
Chase: "The F is silent, like in knife."

Turns out the pair have been made honorary spies by Ronald Reagan. He did so after watching the movie 'Spies Like Us'. They explain that during the Cold War, the Soviet Union created American sleeper agents that can be activated by the phrase 'Gosh, that Italian family at the next table sure is quiet' which no-one would ever say. Mayor West is activated when he hears the trigger phrase...
In Mayor West's office...
Dan: "Thank you for seeing us on short notice, Mayor West."
Mayor West: "No

problem, gentlemen. May I call you gentlemen?"
Stewie: "Yeah."

Before West escapes, Ackroyd fastens a homing beacon to him which allows them to follow him... to Russia. In Russia, the four are quickly captured under orders of Prime Minister Vladmir Putin. West launches a nuclear missile aimed for the US. Ackroyd hacks into the missile's guidance system and blows it up.

Back home. Stewie: "Boy, who would've thought all this trouble could be caused by simply uttering the phrase: Gosh, that Italian family at the next table sure is quiet."
Meg's eyes widen, she goes to the phone and dials.
Meg speaks in Russian: "2476 is aware and is awaiting for instructions from our side."
The man on the phone replies in Russian: "Shut up, 2476!"

In other 'Spies Reminiscent of Us' news, Peter, having been told he's not funny by Chase and Ackroyd, decides to set up an Improv comedy

LOIS: "PETER, YOU CAN'T KEEP USING CLEVELAND'S BATHROOM."

PETER: "OH, MY GOD! YES I CAN! CLEVELAND'S BATHROOM IS THE GREATEST DISCOVERY SINCE FAT WOMEN DISCOVERED DIET COKE."

group with Quagmire and Joe.

Peter: "Okay, so we gotta come up with a name for our improv group. Anybody got anything?"
Joe: "How about 'The Joke Ridge Boys'?"
Peter: "Eh. Not bad. Wait, how about 'Funny Side Up'?"
Quagmire: "No, no, no, guys, we've got the name. It's 'Impravda: The Truth is Ad-libbed'."
Joe: "What about 'Deliveries in Rear'?"
Peter: "Oh, yes!"
Quagmire: "No, no, you can't just jam jokes in for no reason. It has to be organic to the situation."
Peter: "What the hell you being so friggin' comedy Hitler about?"
Quagmire: "I was in three improv groups in college, Peter. I was in 'Improvidence', I was in 'Wackadamia Nuts' and I know I'm dating myself here, but 'Three Smile Island'. My point being that I am the only experienced member of this group."

The first performance of 'Room for Improv-ment' doesn't go to Quagmire's plan. Peter takes over the sketch with his John Wayne impressions and Joe defecates. Start with poop. End with poop. Comedy is a simple genre.

SEASON EIGHT

[HIGHLIGHT]

150th Episode
Brian & Stewie!

Stewie and Brian are in a bank safe. As Stewie goes to leave, the door shuts and locks, locking them in. They try calling for help, but to no avail. Stewie poops his pants.

There's an ominous pooey fog in the room. We know don't we, dear viewer, that Stewie can't leave his diaper as it is? What to do, what to do...? Stewie asks Brian to eat his poop.

Brian is repulsed. Now let's face it, it's not even a great thing to watch, never mind actually do. Brian says he'd rather shoot himself than eat Stewie's poop. He has a gun? In his safety deposit box? Why would you have a gun in your

safety deposit box, Brian? Stewie wrestles the gun away from Brian and threatens him – it's poop eatin' time.

"What I would need you to do is eat what is in my diaper, lick the diaper clean, possibly lick my butt and then put the diaper back on me... Probably lick my butt... Yeah you should start wrapping your brain around that too. And just do me a favour and tell me when you're about to begin because I don't wanna be surprised - Mooooon Riiiiiver. My god! There it goes! Haa, Brian you rock, thank you so much for doing this."

Brian forces himself to eat the poop, the sight of which causes Stewie to vomit. Brian now eats the vomit.

Come on, it's throw up. You like throw up... Is your face slightly contorted reading this? Our faces are. It's funny, sure, but it's also kinda sick, isn't it? Funny sick.

There's liquor in Brian's safety box, which he swigs

from. Stewie, who drinks some alcohol too, isn't really scared that Brian will try something, but he does give him a warning. Brian is bemused: "Try what? I already practically French kissed your butt."

After Brian pierces Stewie's ear, Stewie asks if the dog whisperer is real and the two get into an argument over whether a dog's life has any purpose. Brian takes offence and says Stewie looks gay in his sweater. It's time for Stewie to take Brian down. Down to Chinatown...

"You think I care about you? I don't. You're just smart enough and you're just clever enough to occasionally amuse me. If I had anybody else, ANYBODY else to choose from, I would. You are the best of a bad situation. Nothing more. I use you, man. I got you to eat my poop. And you know why I did it? Because I wanted to see if I could. I thought, how low can I get this douchebag to go... and

" YES BUT A GUN IT'S SO MESSY. WHAT ABOUT PILLS? EVEN HANGING YOURSELF IS BETTER, AT LEAST THEN YOU MIGHT GROW AN INCH OR TWO WHILE YOU'RE HANGING THERE. OF COURSE WHEN THEY FIND YOU, YOU MIGHT HAVE THOSE ILLEANA DOUGLAS EYES. "

when you did it? I actually felt sorry for you. There you go, your turn."

They see a security camera and Brian realises his dog-baby-heiny-lick is going to be on YouTube.

They fall asleep. Waking up, Brian breaks down, life is just too much. He can't find meaning in his life. He confesses he has a gun in case he ever wants to commit suicide.
Stewie: "Wow. Oh... oh my God. You're serious, but why Brian?"
Brian: "You wouldn't understand, you're just a kid."
Stewie: "I could try."
Brian: "I don't know, sometimes it's all too much."
Stewie: "What is?"
Brian: "Life. Everything. Just having the gun here, knowing there's a way out – it helps."
Stewie: "Yes but a gun it's so messy. What about pills? Even hanging yourself is better, at least then you might grow an inch or two while you're hanging there. Of course when they find you, you might have those Illeana Douglas eyes."

The show ends with Stewie claiming that, truthfully, Brian is his only friend, that Brian gives Stewie's life purpose. Sentimentalism and poop-eatin'.

SEASON EIGHT

[HIGHLIGHT]

Go Stewie Go!

With a lipstick smeared nod to Tootsie and Mrs. Doubtfire, Stewie dresses up as a girl to land a role on his favourite TV show, Jolly Farm. With all the male parts cast, he becomes Karina Smirnoff and fools the auditioning panel (and Brian) into thinking he's a girl. When it is time for Stewie to do his line 'that sounds like fun', he swaps it instead for a monologue on powerful women. Amazingly, he becomes a hit.

On set, Stewie becomes smitten with his co-star Julie.
Stewie: "Because, I think I'm in love with her. Whenever I talk to her, it makes my bandaid start to peel off."
Brian: "What are you talking about?"
Stewie: "I'm talking about my thing. I gotta hide it for the

cameras. Instead of tucking, I just push it in like a button and put a band-aid over it."

Brian: "What kind of band-aid?"

Stewie: "A big one, big giant one. Nah, just one of those dots you put on a shot."

Julie calls by unexpectedly asking for Karina. Stewie runs upstairs and, to keep up the façade, has to do a quick change...

Stewie: "Karina!"

Karina: "Yes?"

Stewie: "You have a visitor."

Karina: "Who is it?"

Stewie: "Oh it's that nice girl Julie, from your show."

Karina: "Oh Julie. Did she say what she wanted?"

Stewie: "Oh just go and see for yourself, I'm not your secretary, Karina."

Karina: "Why are you so cruel to me? Is it because I'm the pretty one? The talented one?"

Stewie: "Oh for God's sakes. You know we're all sick of you Karina! That's right, all of us."

Karina: "Sick of me? Oh that's rich! You know, I wasn't going to say this, but mother hates you!"

Stewie: "That's not true! You take that back!"

Karina: "It is true, she hates you. She told me. It was the Christmas we all went to Enavale Railroad, and you cried because you were afraid because one of Santa's elves was a real midget, and father said 'That's it! I can't take this anymore!' and he left that very night! And all you cared about was ice cream on the way home. And mother said you didn't appreciate anything..."

Brian: "KARINA!"

Karina: "Coming!"

They have a sleepover. Stewie exposes himself as a boy. The end.

Meanwhile... Peter notices Lois has a grey hair: "Lois, you have a grey hair."

Lois: "What?"

Peter: "Inch and a half left of your part."

Lois: "Oh my god, you're right."

Peter: "You know I don't mind so much that you're aging, it's just the way you're shoving it down my throat."

Meg gets a new boyfriend, Anthony. Lois, feeling her age, lusts after him while Peter admits a newfound respect for Meg:

STEWIE: "BRIAN, I THINK I'M IN LOVE WITH JULIE. WHENEVER I TALK TO HER, IT MAKES MY BANDAID START TO PEEL OFF."

"You know, for the first time, I am attracted to my daughter. This is what other fathers must feel like."

Anthony tells Lois she is pretty enough to be a movie star, but Peter puts him straight pretty darn quick: "Look Anthony, trust me, she ain't what she used to be, alright? Once you get those pants off it's like two sagging pressed hams and a slice of pizza."

Lois, infatuated with Anthony, passes him a schedule of when Peter will not be at home: "My menstrual cycle's on there too, but I don't mind if you don't." Meg catches Lois making out with Anthony.

When Lois goes to apologise for stealing Anthony. Meg, is outraged: "You couldn't steal him from me..." Lois replies: "Well, I do know a few things...

"You couldn't even imagine the things I do for him. And this isn't about making out. This is about power tools.

"I go to places you couldn't get back from. I'll do anything. You don't know me."

Meg rips out her own tooth. "He hangs me from the shower rod with your old bras and then we laugh at you. Now get out of my room!"

The Splendid Source

Peter and Lois are in the kitchen discussing a trip to Maine when Chris comes in and tells them he's suspended for telling a dirty joke in class... "Was it the one where the blind guy goes past the fish market and says 'good morning ladies'?" Chris reveals it was Quagmire who told him the joke in the first place.

Quagmire tells Peter the joke. Peter finds the joke so funny, every time he hears it, he accidentally poops himself - even when asleep. "When you poop in your dreams you poop for real."
Peter wants to know where Quagmire heard the joke.

Bruce told him the joke. And so began their journey to find the splendid source of all off-colour humour as we know it.
Peter, Quagmire and Joe locate Bruce at the bowling alley and ask him to tell them where the joke came from.

"Oh no... I'm not going to tell y'all that one here at the workplace, too dirty." Joe isn't happy: "Look, you blade, just tell us who you heard it from!"

Bruce had heard it from Consuela, who heard it from Mayor West, who heard it from Dr. Hartman, who heard it from Angela, who heard it from Opie, who heard it from Herbert, who heard it from Tom Tucker, who heard it from Bender on Futurama, who heard it from Al Harrington, who heard it from REO Speedwagon, who heard it from a Bar Tender in Virginia!

Meanwhile, the girls still think they're going to Maine on vacation so, in the car, Quagmire has to distract them with questions: "Say ladies, I wonder if you can tell me, what was childbirth like? Have you girls ever worked in an office with other women who you had negative things to say about?"

When they reach Virginia,

they discover it was Cleveland who told Gus the Bartender the joke! Cleveland invites the Griffins, the Swansons and Quagmire round for dinner.

Peter tells Cleveland: "Hey, you know, Cleveland, you better hide the markers from your kids. Somebody coloured in your Jesus." Rallo don't like that: "Somebody coloured in your ass with too much ass, fat-ass."

Cleveland tells Peter a bellhop at the Royale Hotel in Washington, Sal Russo, told him the joke. On the way to Washington, Peter, Joe, Cleveland and Quagmire are shot at.

When they get to Washington, Sal won't tell them the origin of the joke and tries to escape. The quartet is captured by men in black suits and flown to a large stone temple where The Dean of the Secret Order of Dirty Joke Writers appears!

Inside the stone temple is a library of all the world's dirty jokes and their writers.

PETER: "HEY, YOU KNOW, CLEVELAND, YOU BETTER HIDE THE MARKERS FROM YOUR KIDS. SOMEBODY COLOURED IN YOUR JESUS."

RALLO: "SOMEBODY COLOURED IN YOUR ASS WITH TOO MUCH ASS, FAT-ASS."

The Dean tells them that many of the world's greatest geniuses secretly devote themselves to coming up with the world's dirtiest jokes.

Stephen Hawking: "So the housewife tells the plumber, okay, you have cleaned my pipes, now get to work on my sink."

Bill Gates: "Is there a joke area of a beaver eating a woodpecker? Is that something that would work?"

The quartet is told, because they know all the Order's secrets, they must stay there for the rest of their lives. After Peter stabs Cleveland with a pencil, they escape, burning down the temple as they go.

They eventually destroy the temple and get back to Virginia. For those of you who got to the end of this tale, you deserve a reward, so here it is... some footage of an ape scratching himself.

BEHIND THE FAMILY GUY SCENES

So, you think Family Guy just tumbles from a paint pot onto the streets of Quahog do you? Though it may not look like it, Family Guy is painstakingly put together by a team so talented you could sharpen a machete on their cerebellum. We thought we'd sort of take you behind the scenes to meet at least some of the fine men and women who bring Family Guy to the screen.

All About...
Seth MacFarlane

Seth Woodbury MacFarlane was born on October 26, 1973 and is the animator, writer, producer, actor, singer, voice actor, and director for the show.

He's a sci-fi type of guy and has made appearances on Star Trek: Enterprise and was the voice of Johann Kraus in Toro's Hellboy II: The Golden Army. He also sings the opening credits on the film Futurama: Into the Wild Green Yonder.

As a child, Seth drew everything he could find – including Fred Flintstone and Woody Woodpecker. By the time he was nine he was drawing his own character Walter Crouton, a comic strip for the The Kent Good Times Dispatch.

Seth came to Fox's attention after Larry and Steve, which featured a middle-aged Larry and an intellectual dog, Steve (ring any bells).

Fox asked Seth to make a 15-minute short giving him $50,000. He told the New York Times: "I spent about six months with no sleep and no life, just drawing like crazy in my kitchen and doing this pilot." It took him six months.

Seth is equally passionate about gay rights... "Why is it that Johnny Spaghetti Stain in Georgia can knock a woman up, legally be married to her, and then beat the shit out of her, but these two intelligent, sophisticated writers who have been together for 20 years can't get married?" Seth voices Peter, Brian, Quagmire, Tom Tucker his son Jake and Stewie.

All About...
Alex Borstein

Alex Borstein voices Lois Griffin, Tricia Takanawa, Loretta Brown, and Barbara Pewterschmidt. Alex was asked to provide a voice for the Family Guy pilot while working on MADtv. After she first did Lois, she was told: "Make it a little less annoying and speed it up, or every episode will last four hours". Alex has become a producer and staff writer on the show. As an actress, she played the School Principal in The Lizzie McGuire Movie, Halle Berry's friend in Catwoman and an employee at CBS News in Good Night, and Good Luck.

On her MySpace page, Alex

said she would like to meet the following: "Barak Obama, Steve Martin, Gene Wilder, Pat Benatar, Bill Clinton, this girl from 5th grade that I beat the crap out of, sorry about that, Michelle, you were just all up in my face."

All About
Mila Kunis

Mila Kunis, the voice of droning Meg, won the role, in part, due to her performance on That '70s Show. Seth (the boss) brought her back after her first audition and told her to speak slow and more clearly. She was Rachel Jansen in Forgetting Sarah Marshall and Solara in The Book of Eli, she was in Honey, We Shrunk Ourselves and the Angelina Jolie flick Gia.

Did you know she has heterochromial eyes? Yes... one hazel and one green. She describes Meg as the scapegoat. "Meg gets picked on a lot. But it's funny. It's like the middle child. She is constantly in the state of being an awkward 14-year-old, when you're kind of going through puberty and what-not. She's just in a perpetual mode of humiliation. And it's fun."

In 2008, she starred alongside Mark Wahlberg in the action movie Max Payne, playing Mona Sax, a Russian assassin. She has been dating actor Macaulay Culkin since 2002 and is a big, big fan of World of Warcraft

In a recent interview, she was asked to describe her perfect day. She said: "It would be going for a swim, lazing around the house, playing with my dogs, drinking a root beer float, catching up on TiVo, having some food, a glass of wine and calling it a night."

Osbourne or Austin Powers as Dr. Evil's son, Scott. He was in Rat Race, The Italian Job, and Without a Paddle. He is also one of the creators and producers of the stop-motion comedy crap, Robot Chicken.

As an actor, Seth's big break came when he played a 1940s Jewish boy in Woody Allen's movie Radio Days. Seth is a really big wrestling fan. He even competed in the World Wrestling Entertainment's Raw in the main event, six-man tag team match! And won (by disqualification).

All About...
Mike Henry

A native of Richmond, Virginia, Mike graduated from Washington and Lee University in 1988. He voices Cleveland, Herbert, Bruce and The Greased-up Deaf Guy. Mike met Seth MacFarlane at Rhode Island School of Design. At the time he was doing some stand-up, acting and directing short films.

Henry says Cleveland's voice was based on a person who used to play basketball at Maryland. His friend went to the University of Maryland, but the Maryland accent makes Maryland sound like 'Merlin'. He based Herbert on an old man he used to see at a grocery store he worked at. While working on the voice, he would say things an old man would never say,

All About...
Seth Green

Seth Benjamin Gesshel Green, no I am not joking, voices Chris and Neil Goldman. Seth said that, in his audition, he did Chris' voice using an impression of Buffalo Bill from The Silence of the Lambs. He said he wanted it to sound like Chris' voice was coming through the public address system at a drive-thru burger place.

You may have seen him in Buffy the Vampire Slayer where he plays Daniel 'Oz'

BRIAN: "WHOSE LEG DO I HAVE TO HUMP TO GET A DRY MARTINI AROUND HERE?"

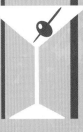

WHATEVER HELPS YOU SLEEP AT NIGHT, BITCH.

like 'why not come down into the basement, I've got a freezer full of popsicles...' and so Herbert became a loveable old funny little paedophile.

On Greased-Up Deaf Guy, Mike said: "We had to come up with a funny picnic gag and 'how about catch the Greased-Up Deaf Guy' came from that."

On working for Family Guy, Mike confirmed: "The best part is everything and the worst part is nothing." Mike described his day thus: "I get to work, go into the writer's room, work on scripts, re-write stuff to make it funnier, record my own stuff and look at story boards just to make sure everything looks right. I work from about 10-6 and wear whatever I want. A lot of celebrities come in. It's a conducive and creative environment. It's different hard work but it's the only thing I would

STEWIE: "DAMN YOU, VILE WOMAN! YOU'VE IMPEDED MY WORK SINCE THE DAY I ESCAPED FROM YOUR WRETCHED WOMB!"

care so much about to do, which is a good indicator of what I should be doing."

All About... Patrick Warburton

Patrick Warburton plays Joe Swanson. Patrick is an American television and voice actor best known as David Puddy on Seinfeld. As a voice actor his unique voice has been used as Ken in Bee Movie, Kronk in The Emperor's New Groove and The Wolf in Hoodwinked.

Family Guy is described by National Review Online as a nasty but extremely funny cartoon. The New York Times call the Griffins an outrageously satirical family and The Sydney Morning Herald name Family Guy a pop culture-heavy masterpiece. The Seattle Times thought it breathtakingly smart and a blend of the ingenious with the raw.

Entertainment Weekly named it the worst show of the 1999–2000 television season and The Parents Television Council said it was the worst prime-time show for family viewing in 2000, 2005 and 2006.

The Parents Television Council regularly criticises Family Guy and once organised a letter-writing campaign to have it removed.

Seth MacFarlane was, as usual, diplomatic and understanding: "That's like getting hate mail from Hitler. They're literally terrible human beings."

Family Guy and its cast have been nominated for 11 Emmy Awards and won on three occasions.

Seth MacFarlane won the Outstanding Voice-Over Performance award for his performance as Stewie.

Walter Murphy and Seth MacFarlane won the Outstanding Music and Lyrics award for the song You Got a Lot to See from *Brian Wallows and Peter's Swallows*.

Steven Fonti won the Outstanding Individual Achievement in Animation award for his story-board work in the episode *No Chris Left Behind*.

The show has also been nominated for 11 Annies, and won three times, twice in 2006 and once in 2008. It has been nominated for a Golden Reel Award four times, winning once.

In 2009, it was nominated for an Emmy for Outstanding Comedy Series. This was the first time an animated programme had been nominated since The Flintstones in 1961.

In the 1,000th issue of Entertainment Weekly, Brian Griffin was selected as the dog for The Perfect TV Family. Wizard Magazine rated Stewie the 95th greatest villain of all time.

In 2009, The Times newspaper rated Family Guy as the 45th best American show. IGN called Family Guy the 7th best animated series. ∎

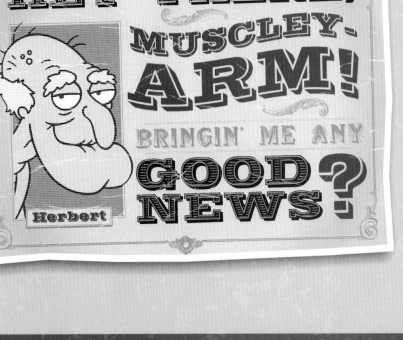

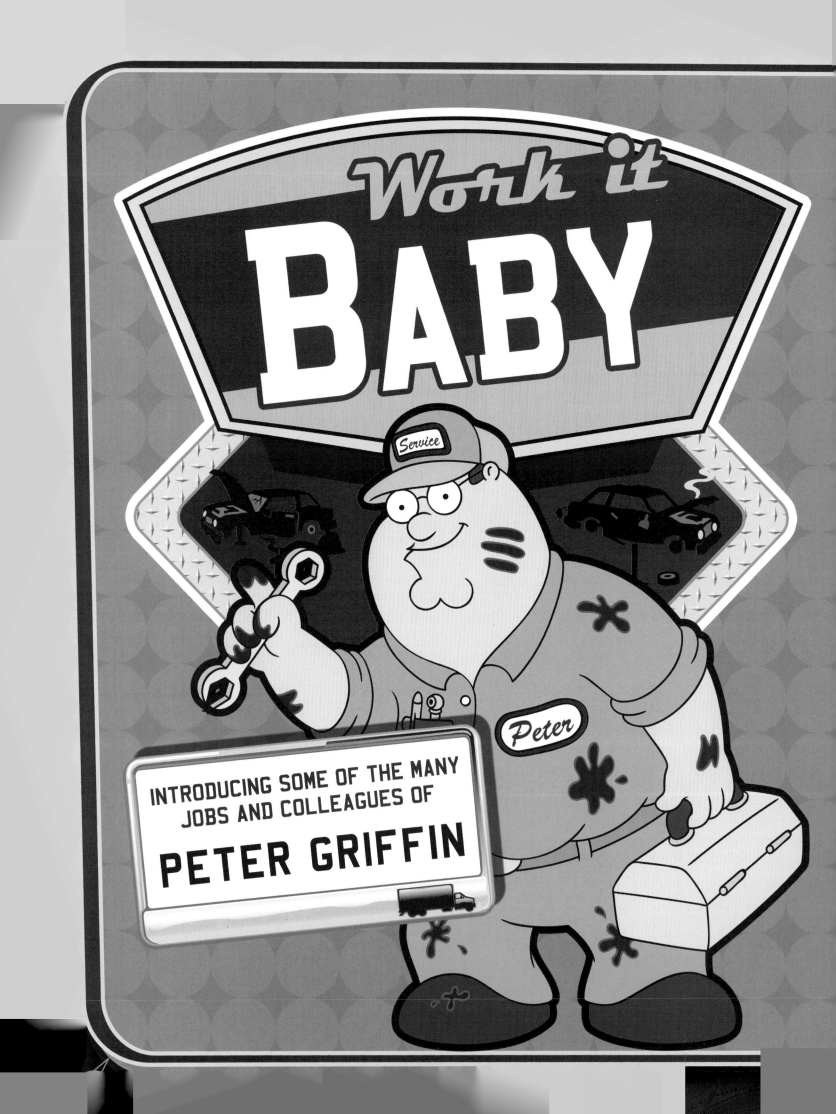

Peter Griffin is most definitely not a workshy fellow... just look at the number of jobs he has had! But ask him to name his favourite employers and we're pretty sure he'd go for The Happy-Go-Lucky Toy Factory and The Pawtucket Brewery.

We say that because they have featured most in Family Guy and without those two places these pages would be blanker than Matthew McConaughey's face at a spelling bee.

The Happy-Go-Lucky factory was owned by Mr. Weed and, for a short spell The El Dorado Cigarette Company, who started making toys to promote underage smoking. You don't need toys to promote underage smoking, just give cigarettes away free with teenage tracksuits, gold earrings and babies.

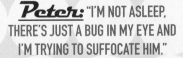

Peter: "I'M NOT ASLEEP, THERE'S JUST A BUG IN MY EYE AND I'M TRYING TO SUFFOCATE HIM."

SOME OF PETER'S MANY ROLES

- ★ Towel Boy
- ★ Assembly worker at Happy-Go-Lucky Toy Factory
- ★ Private fisherman
- ★ Manager of the Shipping Dept at Pawtucket Brewery
- ★ Maid
- ★ Nanny
- ★ Bartender
- ★ Mayor of New Quahog
- ★ Death's substitute
- ★ Theatre Producer/Director
- ★ School Board President
- ★ Reality Show Actor
- ★ Undercover Drug Investigator
- ★ Petorian President
- ★ Tobacco Lobbyist
- ★ Renaissance Fair Jouster
- ★ Bumblescum Sheriff
- ★ Television Producer
- ★ ACME Store Clerk
- ★ Church of the Fonz Priest
- ★ Sumo Wrestler
- ★ Erotic Book Author
- ★ Channel 5 News Special Reporter
- ★ Superstore USA Employee
- ★ Policeman
- ★ Restaurant Owner
- ★ Football Player
- ★ Servant
- ★ Buttscratcher Salesman

Mr. Weed:
"PETER, I LIKE YOU. BUT I NEED YOU TO BE MORE THAN JUST EYE CANDY AROUND HERE."

The El Dorado board bribed Peter by making him President and giving his house a micro-thin coating of Teflon on the inside to make it easy clean.

Making your house clean? Just get a track suited teenage girl with gold earrings, they're not much use for anything else, other than lion food. Yeah, lion food. We know you were thinking it too.

El Dorado also hired a girl to stand next to Meg to make her prettier. You don't need to hire an ugly girl, just any girl wearing a teenage tracksuit, gold earrings and baby. You see what we did there? Did you? Lion food!

Weed is an effeminate weirdo, like Liberace but without the air of sexual violence. Unfortunately, Weed died in the Griffins' home after accidentally choking on a dinner roll. Weed left a videotaped will to be played back to all his employees after his funeral, telling them the factory was going to become the Happy-Go-Lucky Terminal Disease Institute. As a result, Peter lost his job.

Luckily, the Pawtucket Brewery had a vacancy and Peter was put in charge of the Shipping Department. At the Pawtucket Brewery, he

repeatedly gets under the skin of Angela and is regularly outperformed by Employee of the Month, Opie. Opie wears odd shoes, enjoys biting fingers and shoving a pencil into his brain by inserting it into his ear and repeatedly pounding his head on a desk and runs around yelling wablu! Must be like the Oval Office.

At work, Peter also farts very loudly, which is more a lifestyle choice than an occupation, true, but did you know Peter's farts are so wallpaper-strippingly powerful and noxious, that they make people vomit? They make people vomit.

Recently, Peter's career prospects have gone up up, because of his head spinning beauty! Angela is obsessed by Peter but he could never cheat on Lois. However, his alter ego is suave, sophisticated and stuck in the 1920s... "Mmm... I am Mr Reginald New York Knickerbocker. Mmm, what a beautiful shade of lipstick on those teeth... Bleeding gums from aggressive gingivitis? Mmm... well, your mouth is obviously too sweet for your teeth to want to stay in." Peter is going places. ■

Peter:
"MR. WEED? THIS IS PETER GRIFFIN. I WILL NOT BE COMING TO WORK TODAY. I WAS IN A TERRIBLE PLANE CRASH. MY ENTIRE FAMILY WAS KILLED AND I AM A VEGETABLE."

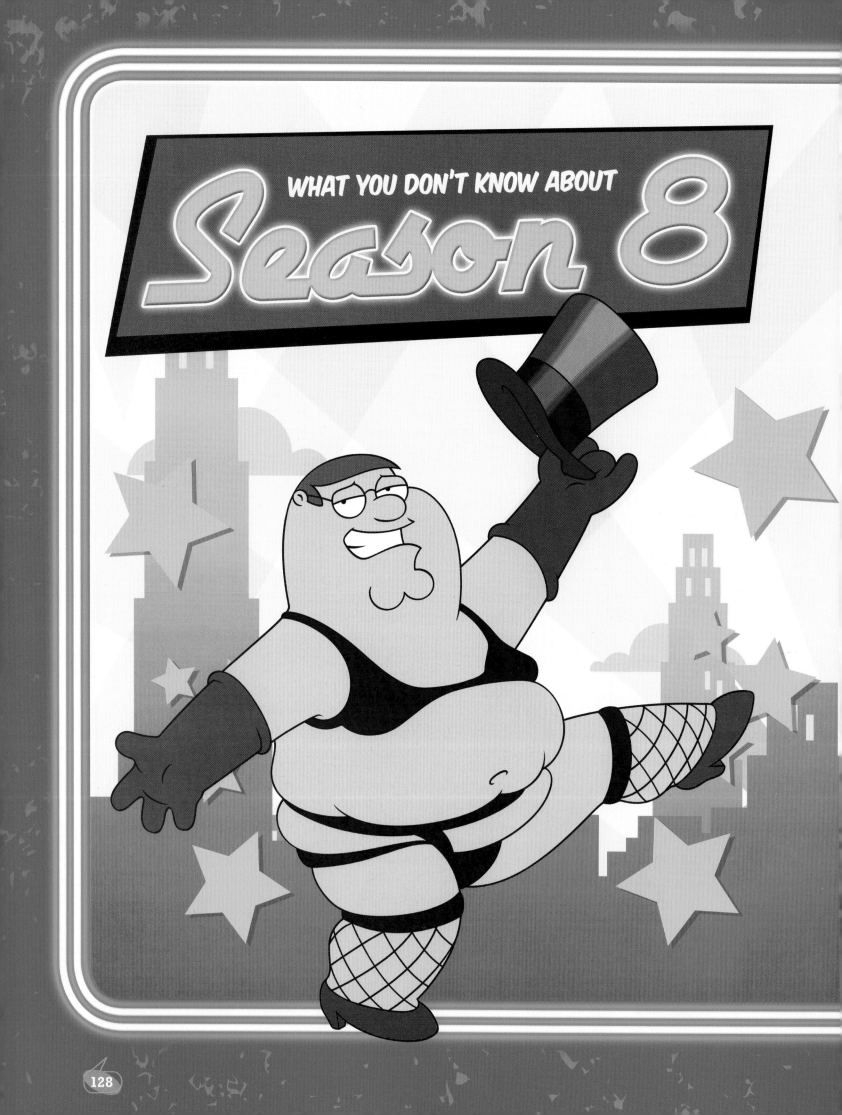

WHAT YOU DON'T KNOW ABOUT

Season 8

Season Eight has more side gags than a hostage with a mis-shapen head, more Raiders of The Lost Ark references than King Solomon's Mines and more double entendres than a Benny Hill skit. But did you spot them all? The nod to Steinbeck? The misquoted Thoreau? It ain't just all poop and pee folks. Though it's mainly poop and pee. Here's our Season Eight list of things you might have missed along the way...

ROAD TO THE MULTIVERSE

☆ *Road to the Multiverse* references the science fiction TV show Sliders. In fact, the episode was very nearly called 'Sliders' but the Family Guy writers decided they needed something more original.

☆ In the Dog Universe, when Stewie says "I hope this next leap will be the leap home", it's the tagline from Quantum Leap.

☆ In the Japanese Universe, Brian's collar contains the character of 'dog'.

☆ The song that plays while Sexy Meg walks down the street is Van Halen's Drop Dead Legs.

☆ In the Two-Headed Universe, the Griffin house features a picture of Chris with only one head.

☆ The Ice Age Universe was originally going to be the 1980s Bullies Universe.

☆ This is Cleveland's last time as a regular Family Guy cast member before he moved to Stoolbend, and his own show.

☆ In the Two-Headed Universes, most characters have their Happy Head on the right and their Sad Head on the left – Stewie's French kissing heads are the other way around.

☆ In the Dog World, Lois is a cocker spaniel, Chris a sheepdog, Meg a British bulldog, Stewie a poodle, Joe a Doberman Pinscher and Tom Tucker is a mongrel.

FAMILY GOY

☆ In the opening sequence, Peter is Superman, Brian and Stewie are Batman and Robin, Lois is Wonder Woman, Chris is Aquaman, and Meg is... Meg.

☆ In the scene at the Drunken Clam when Peter gets the cut out of Kathy Ireland he sings Billy Ocean's 1984 hit, Suddenly.

☆ When Peter shoots at Lois who's picking up the mail, it is a nod to Steven Spielberg's Schindler's List – see how he puts down his cigarette?

☆ When interrupted by Meg during prayer, Stewie removes Meg's heart using Kalimaaaaaa!!! a reference to Indiana Jones and the Temple of Doom.

JEROME IS THE NEW BLACK

☆ Half way through the show, an animation of the Macintosh cursor appears with Peter mid-sentence. He has to wait for it to go.

☆ Jerome and Quagmire quote jive talk from the movie Airplane!

☆ When Jerome says "What 'chu talking about, Peter?" It's a reference to the show Diff'rent Strokes.

APRIL IN QUAHOG

☆ Montecore the lion is named after the tiger that attacked Roy from Sigfried and Roy.

☆ When Mayor West flies up to the constellation Orion, he hits the stars and makes them take on the form of the logo of Orion Pictures.

☆ At the end, Peter is playing Call of Duty: Modern Warfare 2 on XBOX Live.

HANNAH BANANA

DOG GONE

☆ Stewie's phone number is (401) 555-0183. 401 is the actual area telephone code for the state of Rhode Island, where Family Guy is set.

☆ When Consuela shouts "Afuera" at Brian, it is Spanish for outside.

☆ This is one of the very few episodes where Brian is seen without a collar on.

☆ When Lois mentions animal rights group PETA, it's a sly jab at the New England accent where the letter R isn't pronounced. The conversation is a nod to Forties comedians Abbott and Costello's Who's on First? Routine.

☆ The aria the Italian opera singer sings at the end is Rossini's The Barber of Seville.

PETER-ASSMENT

☆ This episode's opening refers the Terri Schiavo case. Schiavo was in a vegetative state for 15 years while her husband and parents fought over custody. Her parents wanted to keep her alive, her husband wanted to switch off life support. The husband won.

☆ The Guy in the White Hat Griffin, Peter's uncle, is based on the photo of the assassination of Lee Harvey Oswald by Jack Ruby. The real guy in the white hat was Detective James R. Leavelle, who escorted Oswald as he was shot.

☆ This episode is a reference of Hannah Montana – the Banana is reference to the Monkey. Clever, huh?

☆ When Chris flicks HATE YOU on his eyelids, it's a reference to a scene in Raiders of the Lost Ark when a girl does the same with LOVE YOU at Professor Jones.

☆ The scene where the monkey falls off the building and gets saved resembles The Matrix Reloaded, where Neo saved Trinity.

BUSINESS GUY

☆ Hugh Laurie, Dr. Gregory House from the Fox show 'House', makes a cameo appearance as his TV character. Hugh Laurie used to be in a comedy double act with Stephen Fry.

☆ This is the fourth time in Family Guy history that the show's title is self referential. The others are Padre de Familia, Family Gay and Family Goy.

☆ When Carter says: "I'm having a heart attack-ack-ack-ack-ack-ack! You oughta know by now!" It's a reference to the Billy Joel song Movin' Out.

☆ When Peter threatens to fire Lois: "Does the name 'Lacey Chabert' mean anything to you?" It's a nod to the re-casting of Meg.

☆ The Swamp Monster chase is a parody of Scooby-Doo.

☆ At the beginning of the episode, Peter, Lois, Carter, and Barbara are standing still until Peter looks into the camera and realizes the show has already started.

BRIAN'S GOT
A BRAND NEW BAG

☆ When the Griffins are waiting outside the DVD store, there's a poster for Alien and 28 Days Later.

☆ The demons that take away the deceased Willy in the movie 'Ghost', take away Joe Swanson in this episode.

☆ Lucy from Peanuts appears and pulls away a football from Charlie Brown. Lucy is kicked by Peter. Lois also kicks Lucy in Lethal Weapons.

☆ Stewie dreams of having Shia LaBeouf shower him with love.

QUAGMIRE'S BABY

☆ The title references Roman Polanski's 1968 film Rosemary's Baby where Rosemary gives birth to the son of Satan.

☆ Before Peter's Palestinian alarm clock explodes, it shouts "Allahu Akbar!" which translates as Allah is the greatest.

☆ In this episode, it is revealed that Lois was nearly killed giving birth to Chris - she had to be completely rearranged inside and will be lucky to reach 50 – this ruins Stewie's time bomb plot.

GO STEWIE GO!

☆ Go Stewie Go is a reference to the lyrics "Go Tootsie Go!" in the song Tootsie, by Stephen Bishop.

☆ Stewie's female alter ego, Karina Smirnoff, is the name of a professional dancer on USA's Dancing with the Stars.

☆ Stewie's argument with Karina is a parody of Mrs Doubtfire.

☆ When Jolly Farm sing the second nursery rhyme about 'It's raining luggages and babies', they're referring to the Boeing 747 which crashed over Lockerbie and killed almost 300 people.

THE SPLENDID SOURCE

☆ It is Freddy Krueger from The Nightmare on Elm Street movies who Quagmire pays to tell Peter the joke in his dreams that makes him soil his bed.

QUAGMIRE'S DAD

☆ Brian is sick for 29 seconds

BRIAN GRIFFIN'S HOUSE OF PAYNE

☆ During Stewie's space fantasy he is heard reciting several lines from Elton John's Rocket Man.

☆ A poster of Robert Pattinson from the Twilight movies can be seen in Meg's room.

SPIES REMINISCENT OF US

☆ This episode was originally titled Ode to '85.

☆ Peter's bathroom song is Let's Get Loud by Jennifer Lopez.

☆ The Hedgehog in Putin's Russian Cutaway Gag is saying: what kind of idiots would make a porcupine sandwich without bread? These no-good punks! Hahahaha!

☆ Meg's voice actress, Mila Kunis, speaks fluent Russian.

☆ The scene in which Putin takes out a hanger for his jacket? Raiders of the Lost Ark reference.

☆ Charles Bronson's 1977 film Telefon had the same plot as Spies Reminiscent of Us.

BRIAN & STEWIE

☆ This episode was inspired by two episodes of All in the Family: The one where Archie was locked in the basement and the one where Archie and Mike were locked in a storeroom and began sharing dark secrets. There was also a nod to The Twilight Zone episode Time Enough at Last. In Time Enough at Last, Henry Bemis is reading a copy of David Copperfield which Brian is also revealed to be reading

☆ When Brian licks Stewie's buttocks, Stewie sings "MOOOOOOOOOOOOOOOOON RIV-EEEEEEEEEEEEEEEER!" in reference to Chevy Chase's prostate exam in the film Fletch.

DIAL MEG FOR MURDER

☆ The title is a reference to Hitchcock's 1952 thriller, Dial M for Murder.

☆ Brian gets a gig writing for the magazine Teen People - Teen People closed down in 2006.

☆ Meg smashing Peter's teeth on a step is a reference to Spike Lee's movie American History X.

☆ When Meg goes back to James Woods High and whacks the cool kids with a sack of unopened soda cans? It's a reference to the teen drama Bad Boys.

☆ The song playing during Peter's rodeo fantasy is Billy Joel's The Ballad of Billy the Kid.

☆ Dial Meg for Murder's original broadcast date marked the 11th anniversary of Family Guy's first broadcast, Death Has A Shadow - January 31st 1999 and January 31st 2010 respectively.

BIG MAN ON HIPPOCAMPUS

☆ The hippocampus is actually a part of the brain in both humans and mammals that stores long term memory. Damage to this can cause amnesia and stop people retaining new memories.

☆ On Family Feud, Richard Dawson compares the crowd's reaction to the premier of Bob Crane's private movies. Hogan Heroes' actor Crane was noted for filming his lovemaking sessions with men and women.

☆ When, to prompt his memory, Lois shows Peter their beachside honeymoon video, it's a reference of the Corona beer commercials.

☆ When Lois helps Peter remember how to have sex is cut by the FCC – it's Dwayne Johnson who steps in.

☆ This marks the sixth time that Peter has faced Ernie The Giant Chicken on TV.

☆ This is the second episode in which Meg is thrown out of the house for making a sexual joke about her parents. The first was in *Model Misbehaviour*, when she made one about Lois. This time she makes one about wanting to have sex with Peter.

EXTRA LARGE MEDIUM

☆ When Stewie says Ellen, the girl Chris dated, once had a bunny he is referencing Of Mice and Men by George Steinbeck.

☆ The Henry David Thoreau quote that Stewie says is actually misquoted. Stewie says: "I came to the woods because I wished to live deliberately and see if I could not learn what it had to teach and not, when I came to die, discovered that I had not lived." The actual quote is: "I went to the woods because I wished to live deliberately, to front only the essential facts of life, and see if I could not learn what it had to teach, and not, when I came to die, discover that I had not lived...."

☆ After Peter believes he is psychic, the sign at the front of the Griffins' house reads 'Psychic readings by Peter The Mystical'.

☆ Bristol Palin, the daughter of former Republican Vice Presidential candidate, Sarah Palin, was said to be heavily insulted by this episode. At one point, Ellen, the Down Syndrome character, says her mother is the former Governor of Alaska. Sarah Palin's son Trig has Down Syndrome.

☆ The doggy dominatrix is uses a dog whistle while a dog is blindfolded and tied to the bed. It is thought high pitched sounds cause dogs pain.

You want to know why you should keep Mayor West in Office at Quahog Town Hall? He is Quahog's caped crusader, he fights the good fight, safeguarding his beloved home town from the threat of taffy and water shortages, zombies and the sea...

HE'S GOOD IN FRONT OF THE CAMERA

Trisha Takinawa: "Here comes Mayor West himself. Mr. West, do you have any words for our viewers?" West: "Box, toaster, aluminium, maple syrup... no I take that one back. I'm gonna hold onto that one."

HE BELIEVES IN JUSTICE

"We gather today to remember those brave Quahog men that were lost at sea. The Bible declares an eye for an eye, so let us now take our vengeance on this murderous ocean." He starts stabbing the ocean and shouts: "You won't be hurting anyone anymore!"

HE DOESN'T WANT QUAHOG TO BE OVER-RUN BY ZOMBIES

"I am Mayor West, I demand all caskets must be encased in concrete, you'll thank me when no one eats our brains, you'll thank me."

HE IS AN ANIMAL LOVER

"I just bought a Rottweiler, and I need a sign to warn people how dangerous it is. Ah, yes, here it is 'ONE WAY'. People will know if they step into my yard, there's only one way out - in a body bag from dog injuries."

HE IS COMMITTED TO SELF-IMPROVEMENT

Doctor Hartman gives Mayor West the very bad news: "You have Lymphoma. Probably from rolling around in that toxic waste. What in God's name were you trying to prove?" Mayor: "I was trying to gain super powers. Silly yes ... Idiotic ... yes..."

HE IS HONEST AND DECENT

"Well citizen that's an excellent question and I thank you for it. I think it's great that we live in a town where you can ask questions. Because without questions, we'd just have answers, and an answer without a question is a statement."

HE IS QUICK TO ACT

When he sees water going down a drain, he wants to know who's responsible. "MY GOD! Someone's stealing my water! They hit when you least expect it. SHOW YOURSELVES, COWARDS! I've spent $1,000 dollars of the taxpayers' money trying to find these thieves and I'll spend $1,000,000 if that's what it takes!"

HE IS A KEEN GARDENER

He has exquisitely green fingers. He thought he had successfully planted sausage seeds, though it turned out Brian had been pooping on his lawn.

HE IS A LOYAL LOVER

"If I enter Connecticut, I'm entering every state Connecticut's ever been with." When marrying his hand, the priest asked: "If anyone has any reason as to why this marriage should not take place, speak now or forever hold your peace." When his other hand raised, he told it: "Shut up, you had your chance!"

HE IS RESILIENT

He once told Brian: "I should warn you, I have a tiny bullet-proof shield the exact size of a bullet somewhere on my body and if you hit it, I will be unharmed and your plan will be foiled. You will be the laughing stock of me... I am also incredibly crafty. Hey, what's that on the ceiling? HA HA, now I'm over here..."

HE IS RESOURCEFUL

"Fifteen years ago, I swallowed everything I needed to escape from a hostage situation. A life raft and a copy of 1989 People Magazine. Alright Paul Hogan, tell me about the real Crocodile Dundee."

You want to know why you should keep Mayor West in Office at Quahog Town Hall? Just to keep the madman off the streets.

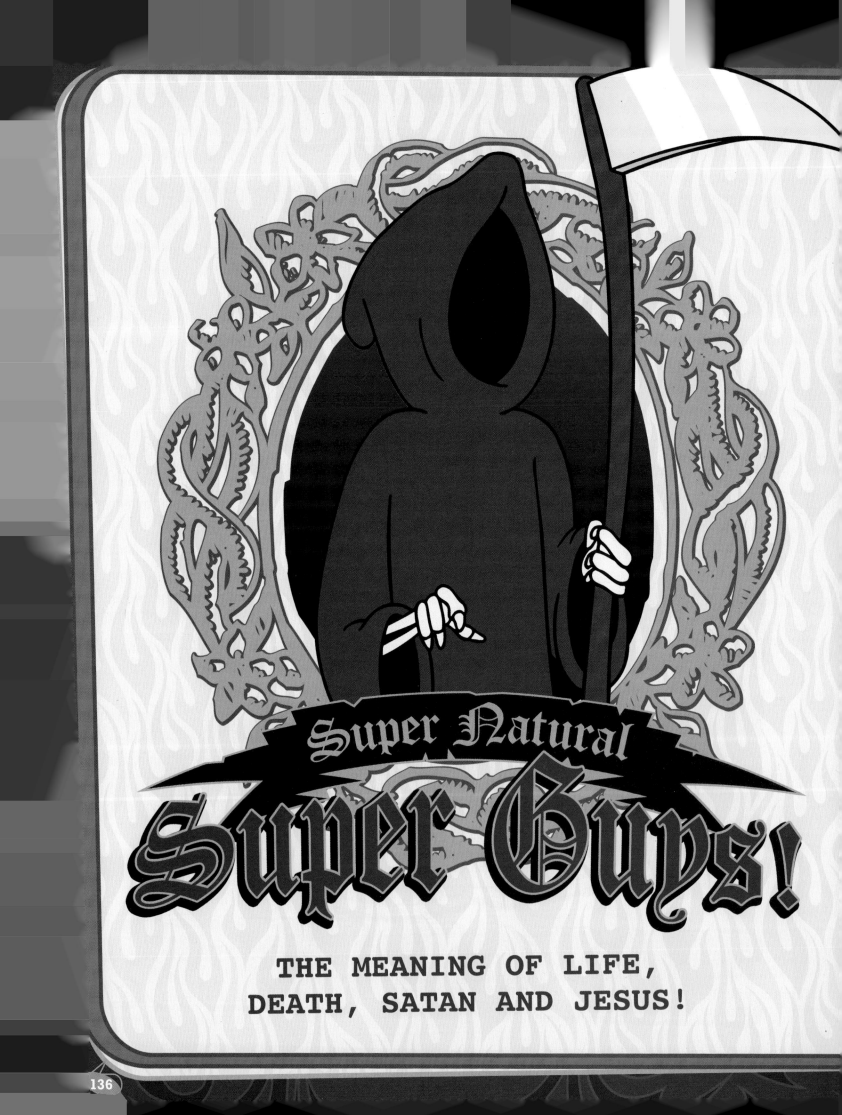

Super Natural
Super Guys!

THE MEANING OF LIFE,
DEATH, SATAN AND JESUS!

You know,

there's a lot of spooky supernatural stuff going on in Quahog, never mind Chris' pants. Let's take Death and Jesus for example. Think of Death and Jesus as two sides of the same coin. On one side you have an empty, meaningless void who preys on the weak and indiscriminately wrecks lives with false promises, on the other is Death.

Jesus may be the Son of God to some, but to the characters of Family Guy, he's just a toga-wearing children's entertainer with little man syndrome who continues to promise to return to earth sometimes soon – like Tom Cruise.

Not believing in Jesus might be okay, but you don't want to start doubting the word of the Lord, now do you? Let's put it this way: I think we could all be confident of beating up our mom, but pops? Biting off more than you can chew – know what we're saying? Here's a thing, if God created the Universe on the morning of the first day, do you think he used ingredients on the back of cereal packet? Kind of explains traffic wardens and paraplegics. Quick tip, the nutritional information on the back of a cereal packet is a low cost alternative to Top Trumps.

Black Jesus: "I rode into town on an ass... YO MAMA'S ASS!"

Something they don't tell you about God is that he's something of a dirty old man using cheap bar gags to try and bed unsuspecting women. He is also regretful about Scripture stories being recorded in modern translations – like that Love thing that they did with The Beatles music. Tragic.

Death? He's a Momma's Boy. He has a skull covered with bugs and snake hair, drives a yellow Volkswagen Beetle and lost his gag reflex due to taking part in films he is not proud of (he can eat a turkey leg off the bone in less than three seconds). Death carries a picture of Edward James Olmos's ass with him everywhere he goes, but then, who doesn't? Death's Mother constantly pesters the boy with maternal concern telling him if he is mean to his mother, a hen will lay eggs in his tummy.

Death's boss – Satan – has already bought Peter's soul for Bee Gees tickets and half of a Mallomar chocolate cookie. Satan spends much of his time scaring dogs with a vacuum cleaner in Doggy Hell.

Lois: "Here, Death. I brought you some Tylenol."

Death: "Oh, great. I asked for Advil, but you know, Tylenol, whatever."

Peter: "I'm not afraid of anything, I laugh in the face of Death. See, Ha Ha Ha Ha."

Death: "Oh great! Thanks a lot. As if it wasn't already hard enough to fit in."

Satan is not the final solution, ironically. He has to answer to Super Devil! Super Devil is six inches taller than Satan, rides a motorcycle and carries a jar of marmalade that forces people to commit adultery. He is good friends with George W. Bush – think of Donald Rumsfeld with horns, and a personality.

SO, YOU THINK YOU KNOW...
QUAGMIRE?

QUESTION 1

What branch of the military was Glenn in?

QUESTION 2

What does Quagmire discover for the first time in *Family Goy*, resulting in a humungous left (!) arm.

QUESTION 3

In *Quagmire's Baby*, what does Quagmire call his little girl?

QUESTION 4

In *PTV*, what is the name of Quagmire's Show?

QUESTION 5

Is Quagmire in his forties, fifties or sixties?

QUESTION 6

At the beginning of *Love, Blactually*, at the party, who is Quagmire dressed up as?

A CONSUMMATE LADIES MAN, QUAGMIRE IS ONE OF THE ONLY PEOPLE TO HAVE AN STD NAMED AFTER HIM. HE IS AN EQUAL OPPORTUNITIES LOVER: HE SLEEPS WITH SKINNY GIRLS, NORMAL GIRL, BLACK GIRLS, WHITE GIRLS, JAPANESE GIRLS, DEUTSCHE GIRLS AND FAT GIRLS (THOUGH THEY HAVE TO PAY). HE KNOWS EVERYTHING THERE IS TO KNOW ABOUT WOMEN, BUT HOW MUCH DO YOU REALLY KNOW ABOUT THE MAN SOCIAL SERVICES CALL 'CASELOAD 451'.

QUESTION 7
What number on Spooner Street does Glenn live at?

QUESTION 8
What does Glenn eat to make himself look younger?

QUESTION 9
Glenn was briefly married to an absolute maniac, what was her name?

QUESTION 10
In 420, Quagmire gets a cat which he absolutely worships. What is the name of the cat?

QUESTION 11
In *Peter's Got Woods*, it is revealed that Quagmire has a son who sports a snappy moustache and pony tail. In which European country does he live?

QUESTION 12
About how many women, according to the Las Vegas CD, has Quagmire slept with?

QUESTION 13
In *Fish Out of Water*, when Quagmire is asked if he could be stuck on a desert island with any woman, who does he say he'd like to be with?

QUESTION 14
What is Quagmire's catchphrase?

QUESTION 15
Which newsreader did Quagmire have a brief fling with?

QUESTION 16
Quagmire's dad had a sex change, what were his pre and post change names?

QUESTION 17
Who is in the picture on the inside of his closet door?

QUESTION 18
In *The Cleveland–Loretta Quagmire*, Glenn sleeps with Cleveland's wife, Loretta. Cleveland and Quagmire eventually make up. At the end of the episode they re-live a famous film scene, which one?

QUESTION 19
In *Baby On Board*, Quagmire reveals the only thing that doesn't turn him on, what is it?

QUESTION 20
What is Quagmire's profession?

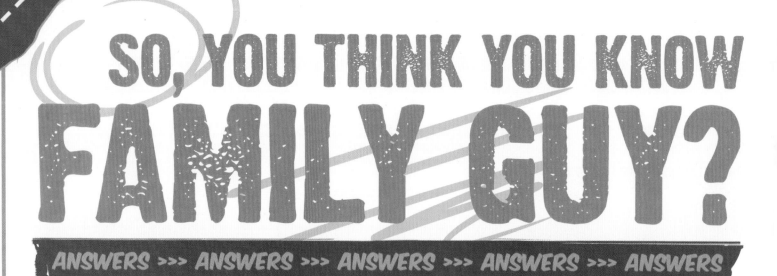

SO, YOU THINK YOU KNOW FAMILY GUY?

HEY, WHAT YOU LOOKING AT? SNOOPING AT ANSWERS HUH? FREAKIN' UNBELIEVABLE. DO YOU SNEAK A PEAK AT YOUR CHRISTMAS PRESENTS? DO YOU TELL CHILDREN THERE IS NO TOOTH FAIRY? NO EASTER BUNNY? FOR THE LOVE OF GOD, NO KNIGHTRIDER?!?!?!

Get back to the pages with the questions and think until you can't think no more. You'll know the time has come when you see a blood bubble inflating in the corner of your eye. Until then, don't darken these pages with your snoopy ways. And we don't mean by defecating all over the bedroom.

SO, YOU THINK YOU KNOW PETER GRIFFIN?

1　His High School janitor
2　Mickey McFinnigan
3　Ernie
4　Mexico
5　Subway
6　Towelboy at the Pewterschmidt's
7　Trombone
8　Piano
9　Sibling Rivalry
10　By shouting 'Shazam!'
11　Bill Clinton
12　Surfin' Bird by Trashmen
13　Gets drunk
　　before taking the picture
14　Director Michael Moore
15　PTV
16　Petoria
17　Mr Weed
18　Big Pete's House of Munch
19　The Fonz
20　New England Patriots

SO YOU THINK YOU KNOW LOIS GRIFFIN?

1　Shoplifting
2　Fat People
3　Alex Borstein
4　Journalism
5　Carol
6　Carter and Barbara Pewterschmidt
7　She had blonde hair
8　She's a Jewish Holocaust Survivor
9　Miss Rhode Island
10　Loose Lois
11　Stuck Together, Torn Apart; Meet the
　　Quagmires; and Big Man on Hippocampus.
12　Diving
13　Brian
14　Me Likey Bouncey!
15　Brain Tumour
16　Black. Baby.
17　Put in his finger and twist.
18　German
19　...to a Protestant Whore
20　Piano

SO, YOU THINK YOU KNOW CHRIS GRIFFIN?

1 Christobel
2 15
3 James Woods High School
4 Hot Dog
5 Evil Monkey!
6 Judaism
7 Chocolate Chip
8 'Mrs Griffin is Hot!"
9 Herbert
10 Connie D'Amico
11 A gay man
12 Police Officer
13 Aquaman
14 Elephant Child
15 Middle
16 Seth Green
17 Cross
18 Mrs Lockheart
19 Killing their sister
20 Alyssa

SO, YOU THINK YOU KNOW MEG GRIFFIN?

1 Lacey Chabert
2 Jimmy Fallon
3 Connie D'Amico
4 Neil Goldman
5 Kevin
6 The Griffin's kitchen is submerged and Peter asks her to rescue a case of beers.
7 House Cat
8 'Get Out'
9 Luke Perry
10 36D
11 Ron
12 Jeff Campbell
13 Her singing voice
14 Oldest
15 Craig (Hoffman)
16 Sarah
17 Throwing Lemonade in her face.
18 Brian
19 He is a corpse.
   (You're such a good listener)
20 James Woods High School

SO YOU THINK YOU KNOW STEWIE GRIFFIN?

1 Bertram
2 Rupert
3 Olivia
4 Rex Harrison
5 Jolly Farm Revue
6 Tuba
7 His 'Coin Purse'
8 Susie Swanson
9 By moving the baseball bat in his toy bin
10 Loismustdie@yahoo.com
11 Gilligan
12 One-year
13 Road to Europe, Road to Rhode Island, Road to Rupert, Road to Germany, Road to the Multiverse.
14 Mr. & Mrs. Smith
15 Bitch-Stewie
16 Omnipotent Overlord of the World
17 Good Night Moon
18 Through his tearduct
19 Stewie and The Cowtones
20 A mind control device used on a judge to free Peter.

SO, YOU THINK YOU KNOW BRIAN GRIFFIN?

1 Shawna Parks
2 Brown University
3 Sea Breeze
4 Martini - then Scotch
5 Toyota Prius
6 Faster Than The Speed of Love
7 Drew Barrymore
8 Jasper
9 Biscuit
10 Texas
11 50
12 Third Level, GreenBelt
13 William H. Macy
14 Labrador
15 Dylan
16 Marijuana
17 Peanut Butter Jelly Time!
18 Ziggy
19 Windshields on cars
20 He became addicted to cocaine.

SO, YOU THINK YOU KNOW QUAGMIRE?

1 U.S. Navy
2 Internet Porn
3 Annaleigh
4 Midnight Q
5 Sixties, he's 61
6 Napoleon Dynamite
7 29
8 Carrots
9 Joan
10 James
11 Madrid, Spain
12 Over 600
13 Taylor Hanson
14 Giggity, Giggity Goo!
15 Tricia Takanawa
16 Dan and Ida
17 Lois
18 With the two in the boxing ring a la Rocky III
19 When people use the world 'rubbish' to describe 'garbage'.
20 Commercial airline pilot